The Chord Songbook

bob ma[illegible]y

Wise Publications
London/New York/Paris/Sydney/Copenhagen/Madrid

Exclusive Distributors:

Music Sales Limited
8/9 Frith Street,
London W1V 5TZ, England.
Music Sales Pty Limited
120 Rothschild Avenue,
Rosebery, NSW 2018, Australia.

Order No. AM956109
ISBN 0-7119-7832-8

Compiled by Nick Crispin
Music arranged by Rikky Rooksby
Music processed by The Pitts

Cover photograph courtesy of London Features International

Printed in the United Kingdom by
Caligraving Limited, Thetford, Nolfolk.

Relative Tuning

The guitar can be tuned with the aid of pitch pipes or dedicated electronic guitar tuners which are available through your local music dealer. If you do not have a tuning device, you can use relative tuning. Estimate the pitch of the 6th string as near as possible to E or at least a comfortable pitch (not too high, as you might break other strings in tuning up). Then, while checking the various positions on the diagram, place a finger from your left hand on the:

5th fret of the E or 6th string and **tune the open A** (or 5th string) to the note **(A)**

5th fret of the A or 5th string and **tune the open D** (or 4th string) to the note **(D)**

5th fret of the D or 4th string and **tune the open G** (or 3rd string) to the note **(G)**

4th fret of the G or 3rd string and **tune the open B** (or 2nd string) to the note **(B)**

5th fret of the B or 2nd string and **tune the open E** (or 1st string) to the note **(E)**

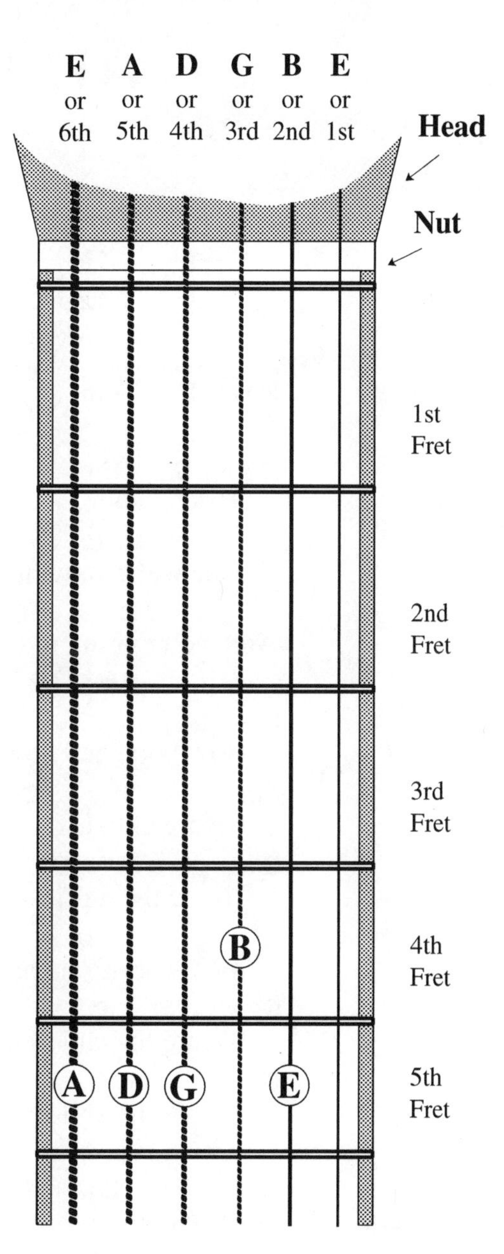

Reading Chord Boxes

Chord boxes are diagrams of the guitar neck viewed head upwards, face on as illustrated. The top horizontal line is the nut, unless a higher fret number is indicated, the others are the frets.

The vertical lines are the strings, starting from E (or 6th) on the left to E (or 1st) on the right.

The black dots indicate where to place your fingers.

Strings marked with an O are played open, not fretted.

Strings marked with an X should not be played.

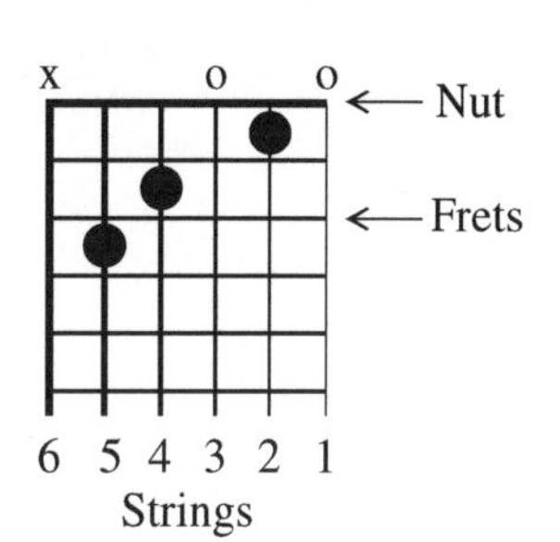

Africa Unite

Words & Music by
Bob Marley

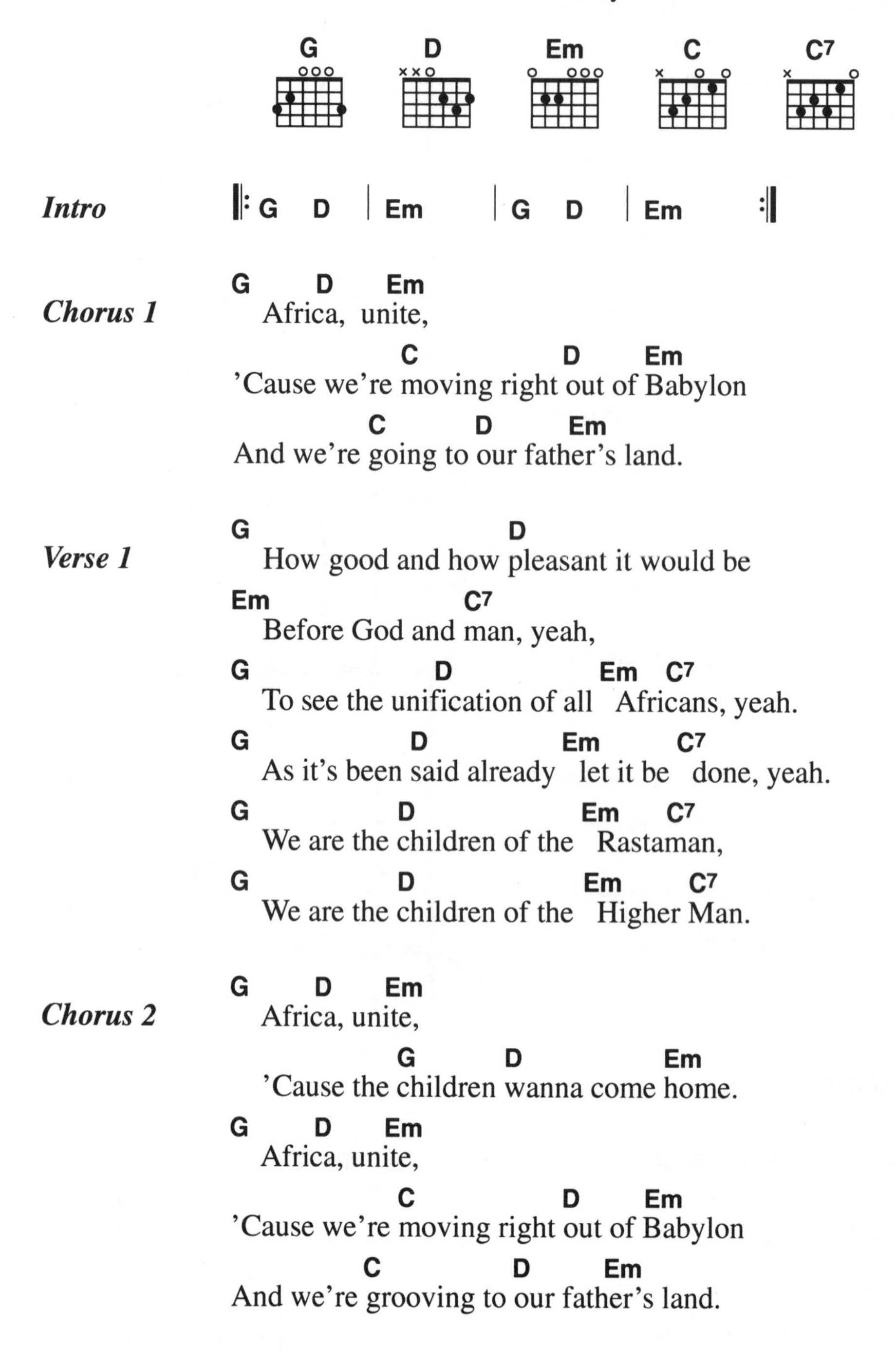

Intro | : G D | Em | G D | Em : |

Chorus 1

```
G    D      Em
  Africa, unite,
                C             D       Em
'Cause we're moving right out of Babylon
             C          D         Em
And we're going to our father's land.
```

Verse 1

```
G                       D
  How good and how pleasant it would be
Em                    C7
  Before God and man, yeah,
G                  D                Em    C7
  To see the unification of all  Africans, yeah.
G                D               Em         C7
  As it's been said already  let it be  done, yeah.
G               D               Em      C7
  We are the children of the  Rastaman,
G               D               Em        C7
  We are the children of the  Higher Man.
```

Chorus 2

```
G    D      Em
  Africa, unite,
                G          D              Em
  'Cause the children wanna come home.
G    D      Em
  Africa, unite,
                C             D       Em
'Cause we're moving right out of Babylon
            C           D          Em
And we're grooving to our father's land.
```

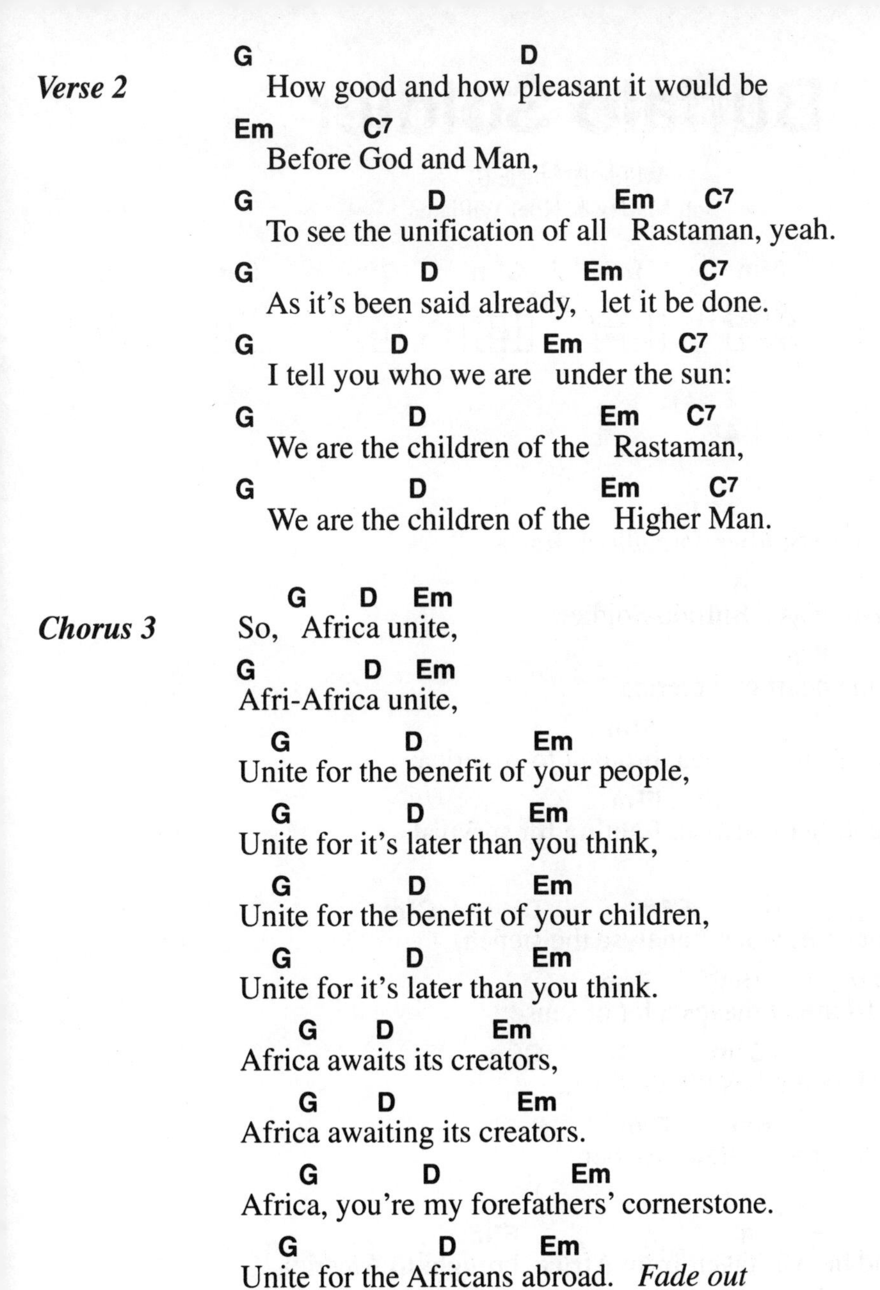

Verse 2

```
G                        D
   How good and how pleasant it would be
Em          C7
   Before God and Man,
G                D                  Em      C7
   To see the unification of all   Rastaman, yeah.
G              D              Em        C7
   As it's been said already,   let it be done.
G            D            Em        C7
   I tell you who we are   under the sun:
G              D                  Em     C7
   We are the children of the   Rastaman,
G              D                  Em       C7
   We are the children of the   Higher Man.
```

Chorus 3

```
     G     D    Em
So,  Africa unite,
G          D    Em
Afri-Africa unite,
   G           D            Em
Unite for the benefit of your people,
   G           D           Em
Unite for it's later than you think,
   G           D            Em
Unite for the benefit of your children,
   G           D            Em
Unite for it's later than you think.
     G     D         Em
Africa awaits its creators,
     G      D         Em
Africa awaiting its creators.
     G         D             Em
Africa, you're my forefathers' cornerstone.
   G             D       Em
Unite for the Africans abroad.  Fade out
```

Buffalo Soldier

Words & Music by
Bob Marley & Noel Williams

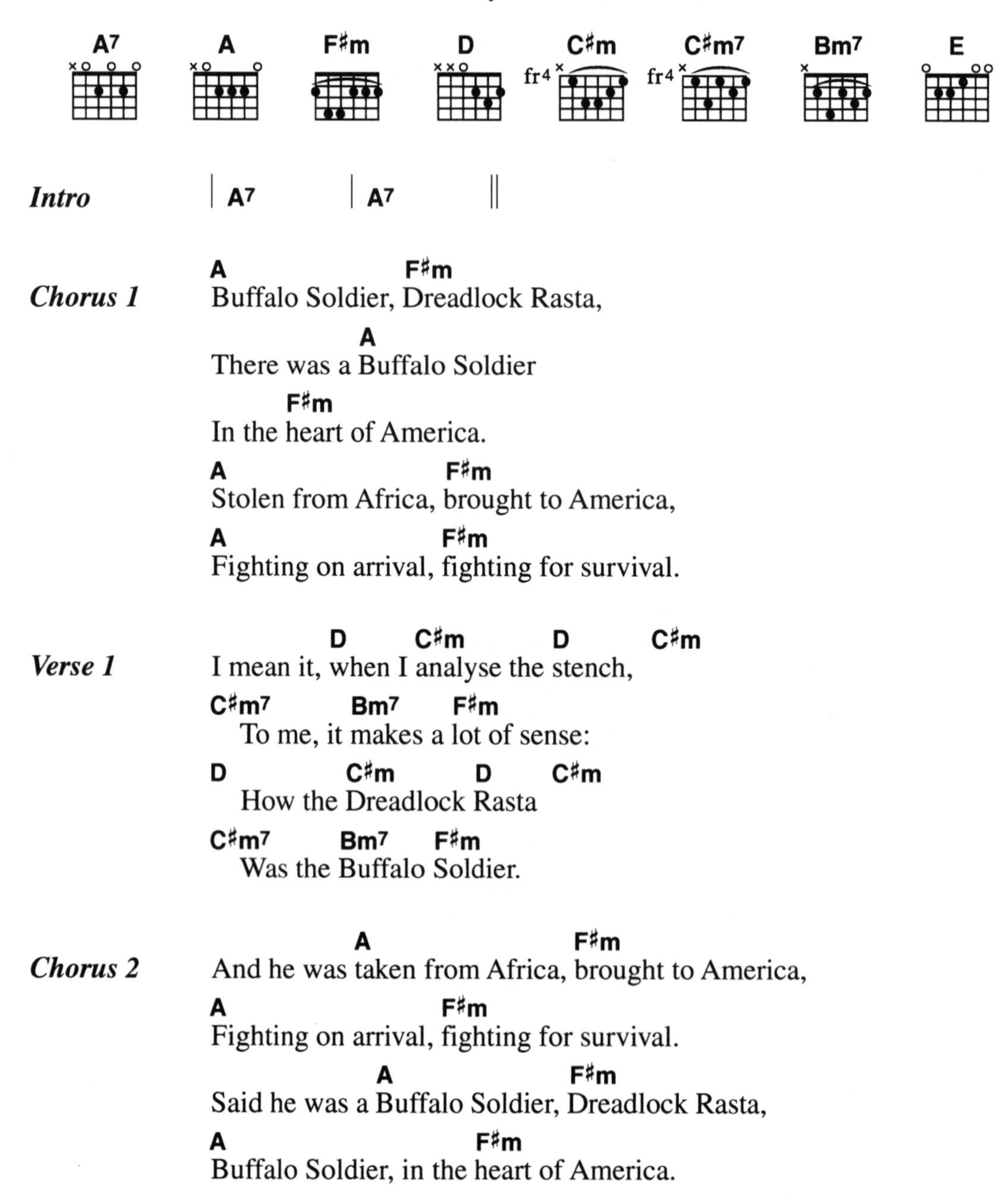


```
Intro        | A7        | A7        ||

             A                F♯m
Chorus 1     Buffalo Soldier, Dreadlock Rasta,
                       A
             There was a Buffalo Soldier
                  F♯m
             In the heart of America.
             A                     F♯m
             Stolen from Africa, brought to America,
             A                     F♯m
             Fighting on arrival, fighting for survival.

                     D       C♯m        D       C♯m
Verse 1      I mean it, when I analyse the stench,
             C♯m7      Bm7     F♯m
               To me, it makes a lot of sense:
             D       C♯m      D     C♯m
               How the Dreadlock Rasta
             C♯m7     Bm7    F♯m
               Was the Buffalo Soldier.

                             A                   F♯m
Chorus 2     And he was taken from Africa, brought to America,
             A                     F♯m
             Fighting on arrival, fighting for survival.
                            A                  F♯m
             Said he was a Buffalo Soldier, Dreadlock Rasta,
             A                       F♯m
             Buffalo Soldier, in the heart of America.
```

Verse 2

D   C♯m   D   C♯m
   If you know your history
C♯m7   Bm7   F♯m
   Then you would know where you coming from,
D   C♯m   D   C♯m
   Then you wouldn't have to ask me ___
C♯m7   Bm7   F♯m
   Who the heck do I think I am?

Chorus 3

                 A
I'm just a Buffalo Soldier
           F♯m
In the heart of America,
A   F♯m
Stolen from Africa, brought to America.

                   A
Said he was fighting on arrival,
F♯m
Fighting for survival,
                    A
Said he was a Buffalo Soldier,
          F♯m
Win the war for America.

Link 1

              A
Said he, woe yoe yoe, woe woe yoe yoe,
F♯m   A
Woe yoe yoe yo, yo yo yo yo.

Woe yoe yoe, woe woe yoe yoe,
F♯m   A
Woe yoe yoe yo, yo yo yo yo.

Bridge

F♯m
Buffalo Soldier,
                              D   C♯m
Trodding through the   land,
                         F♯m
Said he wanna ran,

Then you wanna hand,
                              D   C♯m   E
Trodding through the land, yea, yea.

Chorus 4

(E)   A
Said he was a Buffalo Soldier

         F#m
Win the war for America.

A   F#m
Buffalo Soldier, Dreadlock Rasta,

A   F#m
Fighting on arrival, fighting for survival,

A
Driven from the mainland

       F#m
To the heart of the Caribbean.

Link 2

          A
Singing, woe yoe yoe, woe woe yoe yoe,

F#m   A
Woe yoe yoe yo, yo yo yo yo.

Woe yoe yoe, woe woe yoe yoe,

F#m   A
Woe yoe yoe yo, yo yo yo yo.

Chorus 5

A
Trodding through San Juan

       F#m
In the arms of America.

A   F#m
Trodding through Jamaica, a Buffalo Soldier

A   F#m
Fighting on arrival, fighting for survival.

A   F#m
Buffalo Soldier, Dreadlock Rasta.

Coda

A
Woe yoe yoe, woe woe yoe yoe,

F#m   A
Woe yoe yoe yo, yo yo yo yo.

Woe yoe yoe, woe woe yoe yoe,

F#m   A
Woe yoe yoe yo, yo yo yo yo.

Exodus

Words & Music by
Bob Marley

Am G/B C Dm

Intro | Am | Am | Am | Am | Am | Am ||

Chorus 1
Am
Exodus, movement of JAH people.

Oh yeah!

Open your eyes and let me tell this:

Verse 1
Am
Men and people will fight ya down,

(When ya see JAH light.)

Let me tell you if you're not wrong, then why?

(Everything is alright.)

So we're gonna walk, alright,

Through the roads of creation.

We're the generation, tell me why.

(Who trod through great tribulation).

Chorus 2
Am G/B C Dm Am
Exodus, movement of JAH people,

Exodus, movement of JAH people.

Verse 2

```
          Am
Well, open your eyes (and look within),
Are you satisfied (with the life you're living?)
We know where we're going,
We know where we're from.
We're leaving Babylon,
We're going to our father's land.
```

Chorus 3

```
Am      G/B  C          Dm     Am
Exodus,      movement of JAH people,
Exodus, movement of JAH people.
```

Bridge

```
   Am
|: Send us another brother Moses
(Movement of JAH people),
Come across the Red Sea.
(Movement of JAH people). :|
```

Solo

```
| Am  | Am  | Am  | Am  ||
```

Chorus 4

```
Am      G/B  C          Dm     Am
Exodus,      movement of JAH people,
Exodus, exodus, alright, exodus, now, now now,
Exodus, exodus, exodus, exodus, exodus.
1-2-3-4 move!
Move! Move! Move! Move! Move! Move!
```

Verse 3 As Verse 2

Chorus 5

Am
Exodus, movement of JAH people.

G/B C Dm Am
Exodus, movement of JAH people.

Movement of JAH people, movement of JAH people,

Movement of JAH people, movement of JAH people.

Move! Move! Move! Move! Move! Move! Move!

Verse 4

Am
JAH come to break down 'pression,

Rule equality,

Wipe away transgression,

And set the captives free.

Chorus 6

Am
Exodus, movement of JAH people.

Exodus, movement of JAH people.

Coda

Am
Movement of JAH people, movement of JAH people,

Movement of JAH people, movement of JAH people,

Movement of JAH people,

G/B C Dm
Move! Move!

Am
Move! Move! Move! Move!

𝄆 Movement of JAH people, movement of JAH people. 𝄇

Repeat to fade

Could You Be Loved

Words & Music by
Bob Marley

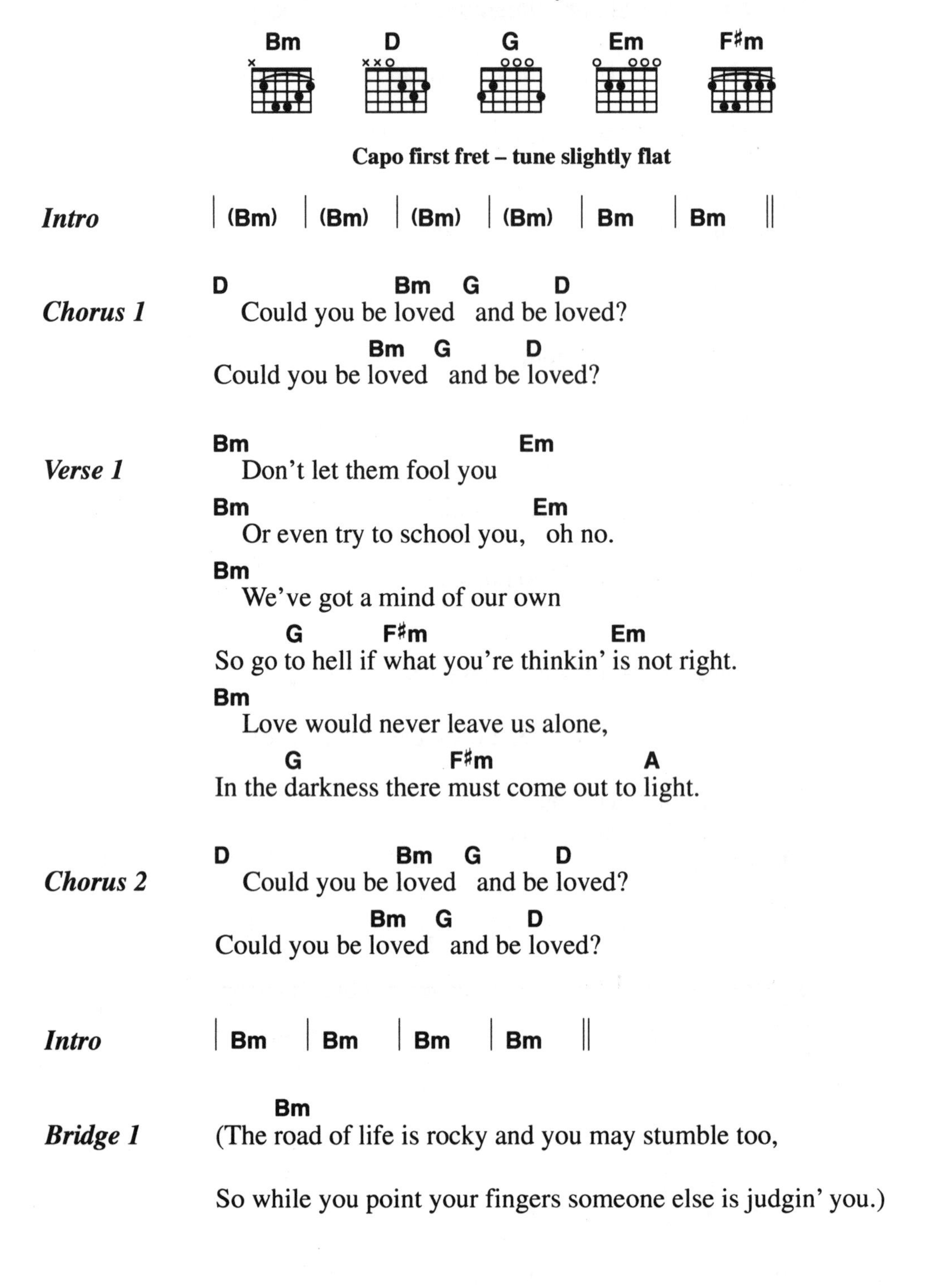

Capo first fret – tune slightly flat

Intro | (Bm) | (Bm) | (Bm) | (Bm) | Bm | Bm ||

Chorus 1

D   Bm   G   D
Could you be loved   and be loved?
               Bm   G   D
Could you be loved   and be loved?

Verse 1

Bm   Em
Don't let them fool you
Bm   Em
Or even try to school you,   oh no.
Bm
We've got a mind of our own
        G   F♯m   Em
So go to hell if what you're thinkin' is not right.
Bm
Love would never leave us alone,
        G   F♯m   A
In the darkness there must come out to light.

Chorus 2

D   Bm   G   D
Could you be loved   and be loved?
               Bm   G   D
Could you be loved   and be loved?

Intro | Bm | Bm | Bm | Bm ||

Bridge 1

      Bm
(The road of life is rocky and you may stumble too,

So while you point your fingers someone else is judgin' you.)

cont.

```
Bm
Love your brotherman.

𝄆 (Could you be, could you be, could you be loved?

Could you be, could you be loved?) 𝄇
```

Verse 2

```
Bm                                   Em
   Don't let them change you, oh,
Bm                           Em
   Or even rearrange you,   oh no.
Bm                            G     F#m  Em
   We've got a life to live (hmm-hmm-hmm).
          Bm
They say   only, only
          G            F#m          A
Only the fittest of the fittest shall survive,

Stay alive.
```

Chorus 3

```
D                 Bm   G       D
   Could you be loved   and be loved?
                 Bm   G       D
Could you be loved   and be loved?
```

Bridge 2

```
Bm
(You ain't gonna miss your water until your well runs dry,

No matter how you treat him the man will never be satisfied.

Could you be, could you be, could you be loved

Could you be, could you be loved?)
```

Coda

```
Bm
(Could you be, could you be, could you be loved

Could you be, could you be loved?)

Say something, say something,

Say something, say something.

Reggae, reggae, say something.

Rockers, rockers, say something.

(Could you be loved?)  Ad lib. to fade
```

Easy Skanking

Words & Music by
Bob Marley

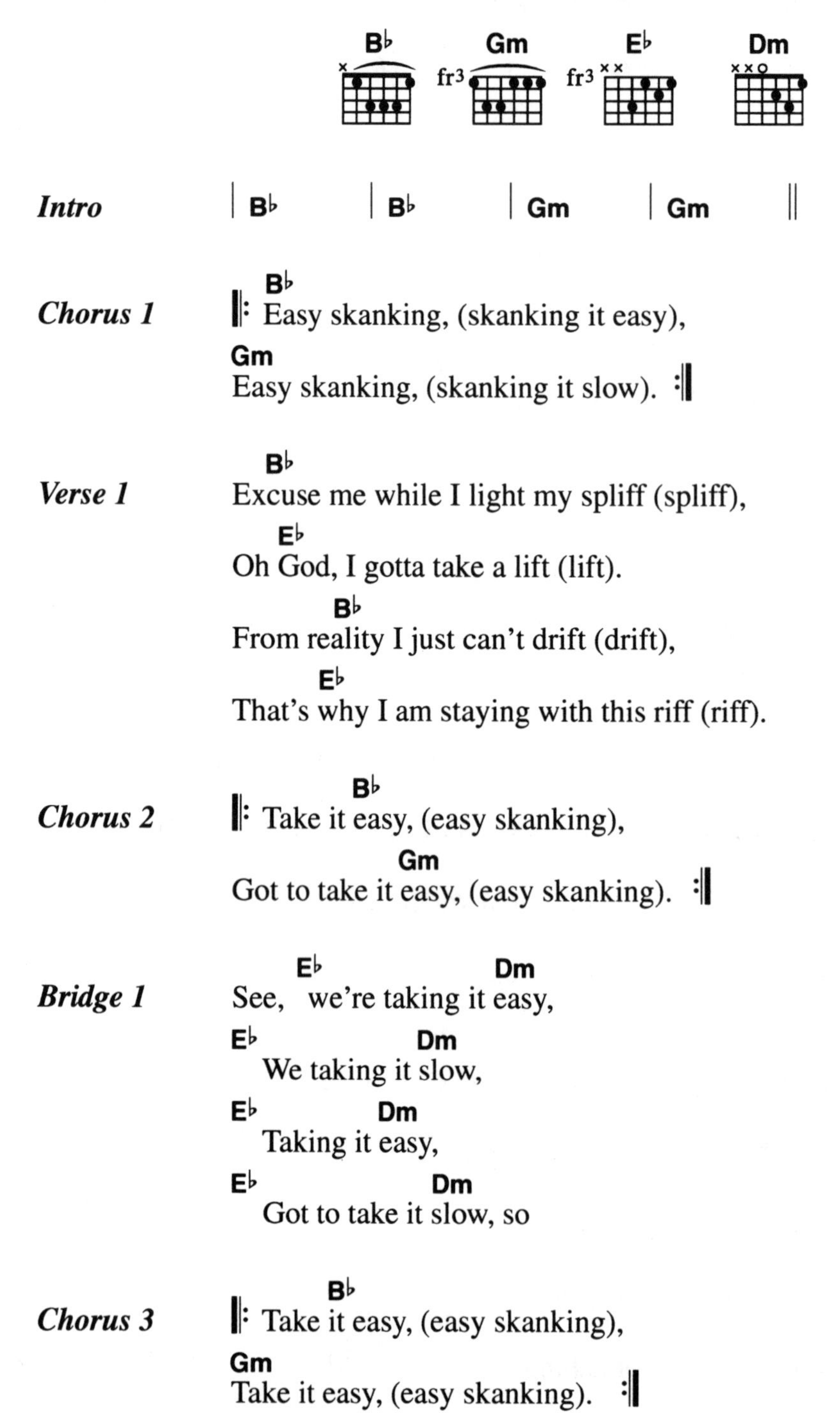

Intro | B♭ | B♭ | Gm | Gm ||

Chorus 1

```
   B♭
𝄆 Easy skanking, (skanking it easy),
Gm
Easy skanking, (skanking it slow). 𝄇
```

Verse 1

```
   B♭
Excuse me while I light my spliff (spliff),
   E♭
Oh God, I gotta take a lift (lift).
          B♭
From reality I just can't drift (drift),
          E♭
That's why I am staying with this riff (riff).
```

Chorus 2

```
            B♭
𝄆 Take it easy, (easy skanking),
                  Gm
Got to take it easy, (easy skanking). 𝄇
```

Bridge 1

```
      E♭          Dm
See,  we're taking it easy,
E♭          Dm
   We taking it slow,
E♭      Dm
   Taking it easy,
E♭           Dm
   Got to take it slow, so
```

Chorus 3

```
          B♭
𝄆 Take it easy, (easy skanking),
Gm
Take it easy, (easy skanking). 𝄇
```

Verse 2

```
        B♭
Excuse me while I light my spliff (spliff),
      E♭
Good God, I gotta take a lift (lift).
         B♭
From reality I just can't drift (drift),
       E♭
That's why I am staying with this riff (riff).
```

Chorus 4

```
         B♭
Take it easy, (taking it easy),
                Gm
Got to take it easy, (taking it slow).
B♭
Take it easy, (taking it easy),
                 Gm
Skanky take it easy, (taking it slow).
```

Bridge 2

```
                    E♭     Dm
Tell you what:   herb for my wine,
E♭        Dm
   Honey for my strong drink,
E♭      Dm
   Herb for my wine,
E♭        Dm
   Honey for my strong drink.
```

Chorus 5

```
          B♭
𝄆 I'll take it easy, (taking it easy),
        Gm
Take it easy, (skanking it slow).
         B♭
Take it, (taking it easy),
         Gm
Take it, (skanking it slow).   𝄇   
```
Repeat ad lib. to fade

Get Up, Stand Up

Words & Music by
Bob Marley & Peter Tosh

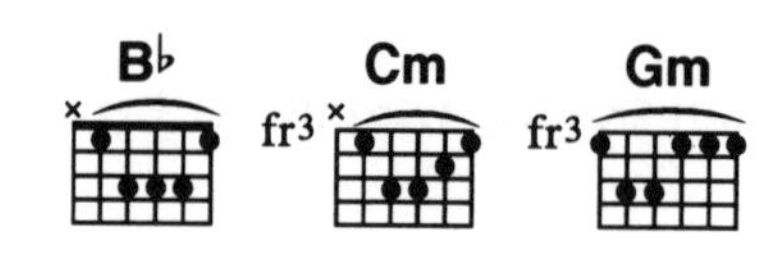

Intro | B♭ Cm | B♭ ||

Chorus 1
Cm
Get up, stand up: stand up for your rights!

Get up, stand up: stand up for your rights!

Get up, stand up: stand up for your rights!

Get up, stand up: don't give up the fight.

Verse 1
Cm
Preacherman, don't tell me,

Heaven is under the earth.

I know you don't know

What life is really worth.

It's not all that glitters is gold;

'Alf the story has never been told:

So now you see the light, eh!

Stand up for your rights. Come on!

Chorus 2
‖: Cm Gm B♭
Get up, stand up: stand up for your rights!
Cm B♭
Get up, stand up: don't give up the fight! :‖

Verse 2

Cm
Most people think,

Great God will come from the skies,

Take away everything

And make everybody feel high.

But if you know what life is worth,

You will look for yours on earth:

And now you see the light,

You stand up for your rights. Jah!

Chorus 3

Cm
Get up, stand up! (Jah, Jah!)

Gm B♭
Stand up for your rights! (Oh-hoo!)

Cm
Get up, stand up! (Get up, stand up!)

B♭
Don't give up the fight! (Life is your right!)

Cm
Get up, stand up! (So we can't give up the fight!)

Gm B♭
Stand up for your rights! (Lord, Lord!)

Cm
Get up, stand up! (Keep on struggling on!)

B♭
Don't give up the fight! (Yeah!)

Verse 3

Cm
We sick an' tired of-a your ism-skism game,

Dyin' 'n' goin' to heaven in-a Jesus' name, Lord.

We know when we understand:

Almighty God is a living man.

You can fool some people sometimes,

But you can't fool all the people all the time.

cont.

Cm
So now we see the light, (What you gonna do?)

We gonna stand up for our rights! (Yeah, yeah, yeah!)

So you better:

Coda

Cm
Get up, stand up! (In the morning! Git it up!)

Gm B♭
Stand up for your rights! (Stand up for our rights!)

Cm
Get up, stand up!

B♭
Don't give up the fight! (Don't give it up, don't give it up!)

Cm
Get up, stand up! (Get up, stand up!)

Gm B♭
Stand up for your rights! (Get up, stand up!)

Cm
Get up, stand up!

B♭
Don't give up the fight! (Get up, stand up!)

Cm
𝄆 Get up, stand up!

Stand up for your rights! 𝄇 *Repeat to fade*

I Shot The Sheriff

Words & Music by
Bob Marley

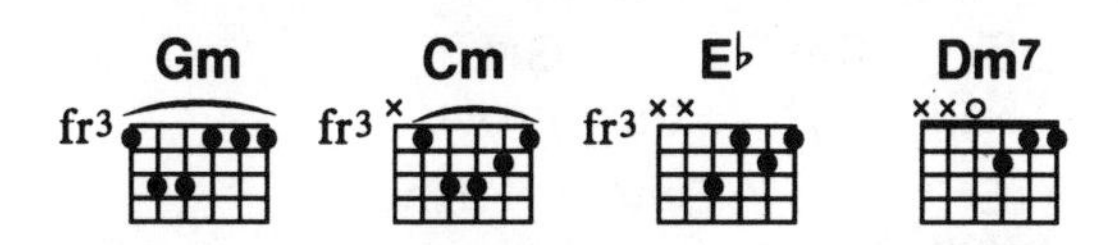

Chorus 1

Gm
(I shot the sheriff
Cm **Gm**
But I didn't shoot no deputy, oh no! Oh!

I shot the sheriff
Cm **Gm**
But I didn't shoot no deputy, ooh, ooh, oo-ooh.)

Verse 1

E♭ **Dm7** **Gm**
Yeah! All around in my home town,
E♭ **Dm7** **Gm**
They're tryin' to track me down;
E♭ **Dm7** **Gm**
They say they want to bring me in guilty
E♭ **Dm7** **Gm**
For the killing of a deputy,
E♭ **Dm7** **Gm**
For the life of a deputy.

But I say, oh, now, now, oh!

Chorus 2

Gm **Cm**
(I shot the sheriff,) the sheriff,
Gm
(But I swear it was in self-defence.)

Oh, no! (ooh, ooh, oo-oh) Yeah!
Cm
I say: I shot the sheriff, oh, Lord!
Gm
(And they say it is a capital offence).

Yeah! (ooh, ooh, oo-oh) Yeah!

Verse 2

```
E♭        Dm7                 Gm
   Sheriff John Brown always hated me,
   E♭     Dm7      Gm
For what,   I don't know:
      E♭      Dm7       Gm
Every time I plant a seed,
        E♭      Dm7          Gm
He said "Kill it before they grow,"
        E♭           Dm7       Gm
He said "Kill them before they grow."

And so, read it in the news:
```

Chorus 3

```
Gm                            Cm
(I shot the sheriff,) oh, Lord!
                            Gm
(But I swear it was in self-defence.)

Where was the deputy?  (Oo-oo-oh,)

I say: I shot the sheriff,
Cm                        Gm
   But I swear it was in self-defence, yeah!  (Oo-oh.)
```

Verse 3

```
E♭                         Dm7      Gm
   Freedom came my way one day
      E♭       Dm7    Gm
And I started out of town, yeah!
E♭        Dm7      Gm
   All of a sudden I saw sheriff John Brown
E♭         Dm7       Gm
Aiming to shoot me down,
    E♭      Dm7             Gm
So I shot, I shot, I shot him down and I say:

If I am guilty I will pay.
```

Chorus 4

```
Gm
(I shot the sheriff,)
      Cm                          Gm
But I say, (but I didn't shoot no deputy,)

I didn't shoot no deputy (oh, no-oh), oh no!

(I shot the sheriff,)  I did!
Cm                         Gm
   But I didn't shoot no deputy, oh!  (oo-oo-ooh.)
```

Verse 4

```
Eb                  Dm7      Gm
Reflexes had  the better of me
     Eb          Dm7     Gm
And what is to be must be:
       Eb        Dm7            Gm
Every day the bucket a-go a well,
Eb             Dm7            Gm
One day the bottom a-go drop out,
Eb             Dm7            Gm
One day the bottom a-go drop out.

I say:
```

Chorus 5

```
Gm                        Cm
I, I, I, I shot the sheriff.
                               Gm
Lord, I didn't shot the deputy.  Yeah!
             Cm
I, I (shot the sheriff,)
                        Gm
But I didn't shoot no deputy, yeah!  So, yeah!
```

Coda ‖: Gm | Cm | Gm | Gm :‖ *Repeat to fade*

Iron Lion Zion

Words & Music by
Bob Marley

F♯m E D Bm A Em

Intro | F♯m E | D Bm A Bm ‖: D | Em | D | Em :‖

Verse 1
Bm
I am on the rock

And then I check a stock,

I have to run like a fugitive

To save the life I live.

Chorus 1
D A Bm
I'm gonna be iron like a lion in Zion,
D A Bm | F♯m E | D Bm A Bm |
I'm gonna be iron like a lion in Zion,
F♯m E D Bm A Bm
Iron Lion Zion. (Li - on!)

Verse 2
Bm
I'm on the run but I ain't got no gun,

See they want to be the star,

So they fighting tribal war.

And they saying:

Chorus 2
D A Bm
Iron like a lion in Zion,
D A Bm | F♯m E | D Bm A Bm |
Iron like a lion in Zion,
F♯m E D Bm A Bm
Iron Lion Zion. (Li - on!)

```
Solo          ||: D     | Em     | D     | Em    :||

              Bm
Verse 3       I'm on the rock, (running and you running),

              I take a stock, (running like a fugitive),

              I had to run like a fugitive

              Just to save the life I live.

                          D          A      Bm
Chorus 3      I'm gonna be iron like a lion in Zion,
                          D          A      Bm     | F#m  E   | D  Bm  A  Bm |
              I'm gonna be iron like a lion in Zion,
              F#m  E    D     Bm  A   Bm
              Iron  Lion Zion.     (Li - on!)

              F#m  E    D     Bm  A   Bm
              Iron  Lion Zion,
              F#m  E    D     Bm  A   Bm
              Iron  Lion Zion.

                 D        A       Bm
Coda          ||: Iron like a lion in Zion. :||   Repeat to fade
```

Is This Love?

Words & Music by
Bob Marley

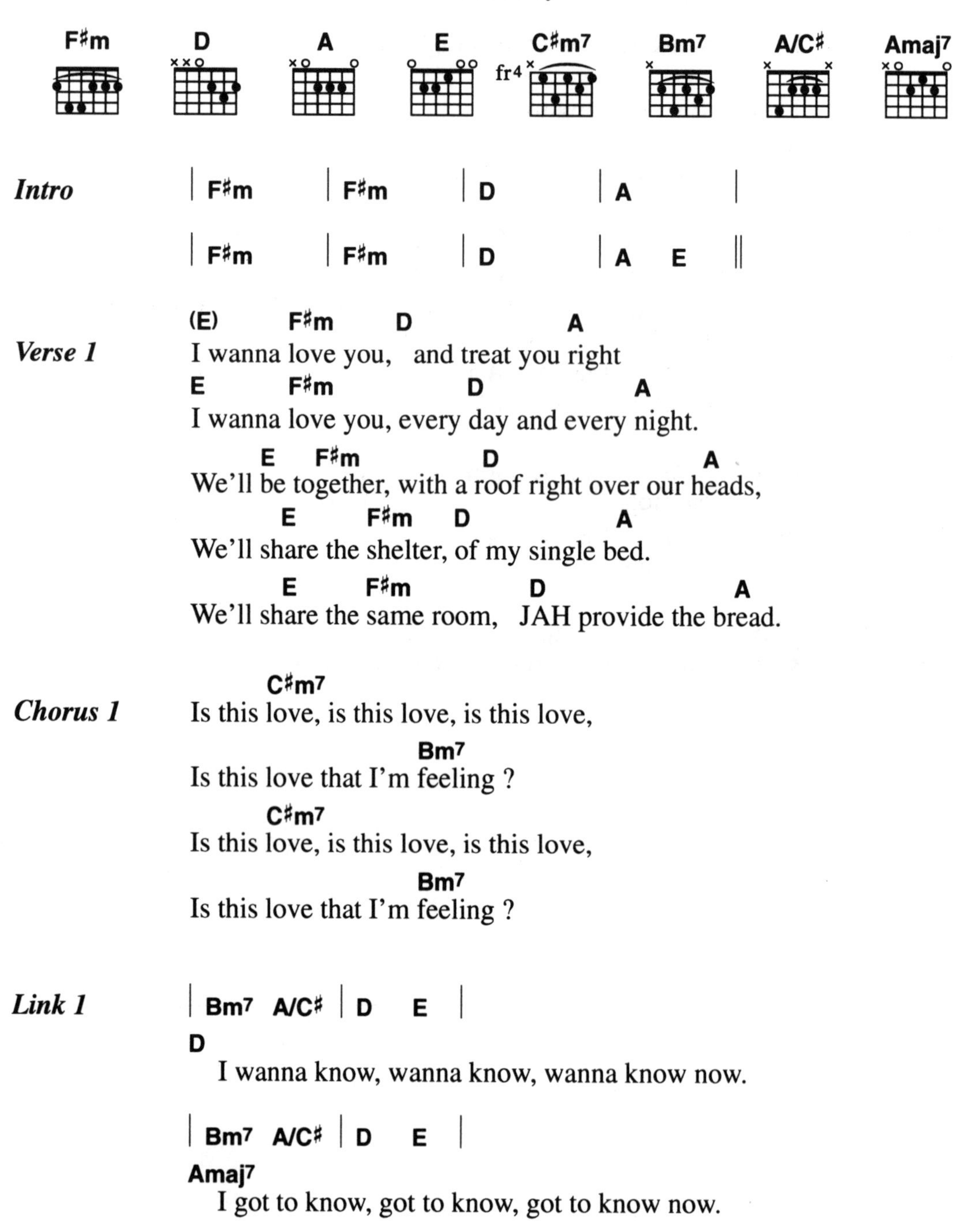

Intro

| F♯m | F♯m | D | A |

| F♯m | F♯m | D | A E ||

Verse 1

(E) F♯m D A
I wanna love you, and treat you right
E F♯m D A
I wanna love you, every day and every night.
E F♯m D A
We'll be together, with a roof right over our heads,
E F♯m D A
We'll share the shelter, of my single bed.
E F♯m D A
We'll share the same room, JAH provide the bread.

Chorus 1

C♯m7
Is this love, is this love, is this love,
Bm7
Is this love that I'm feeling ?
C♯m7
Is this love, is this love, is this love,
Bm7
Is this love that I'm feeling ?

Link 1

| Bm7 A/C♯ | D E |
D
I wanna know, wanna know, wanna know now.

| Bm7 A/C♯ | D E |
Amaj7
I got to know, got to know, got to know now.

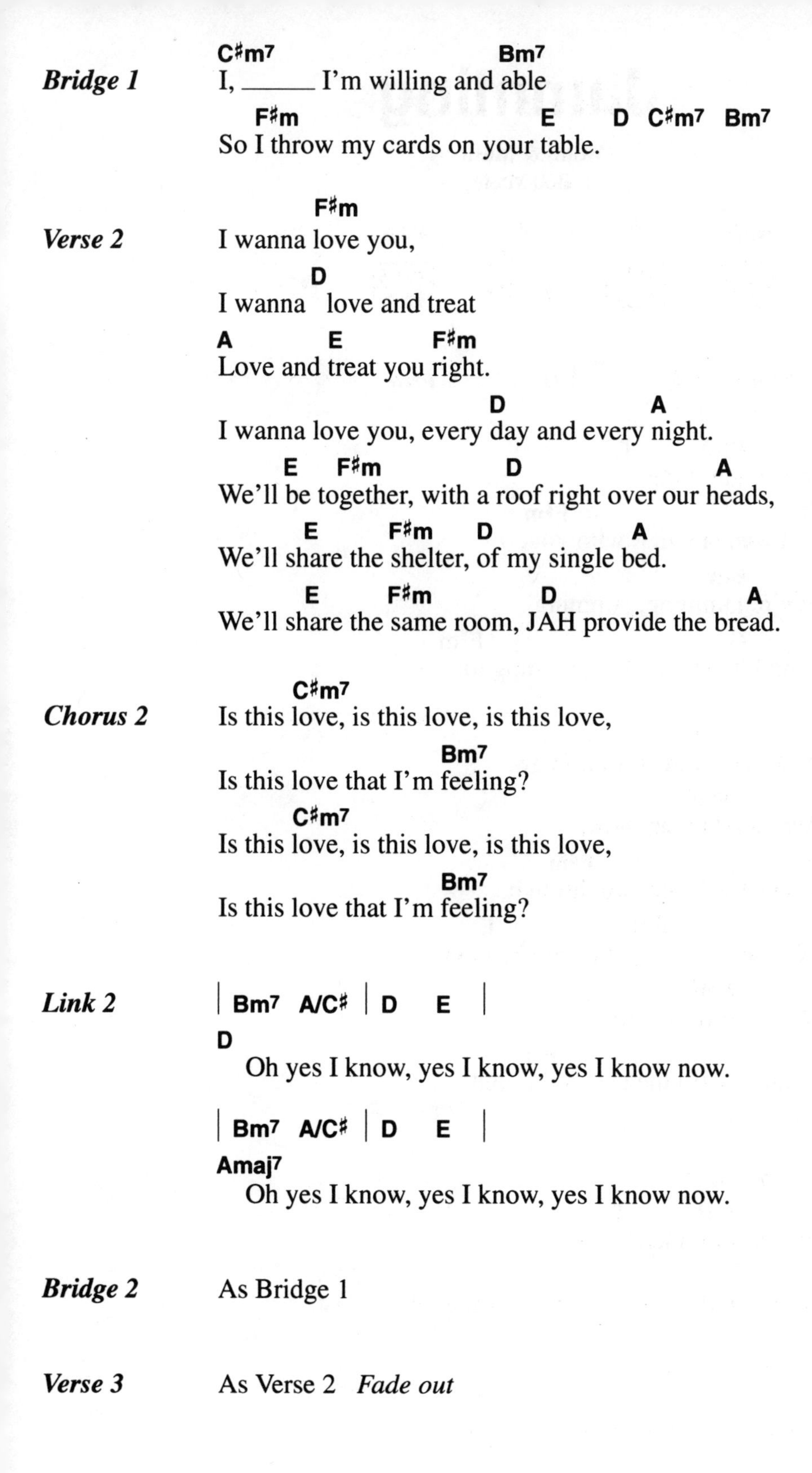

Bridge 1

C♯m7 Bm7
I, ______ I'm willing and able
F♯m E D C♯m7 Bm7
So I throw my cards on your table.

Verse 2

F♯m
I wanna love you,
D
I wanna love and treat
A E F♯m
Love and treat you right.
D A
I wanna love you, every day and every night.
E F♯m D A
We'll be together, with a roof right over our heads,
E F♯m D A
We'll share the shelter, of my single bed.
E F♯m D A
We'll share the same room, JAH provide the bread.

Chorus 2

C♯m7
Is this love, is this love, is this love,
Bm7
Is this love that I'm feeling?
C♯m7
Is this love, is this love, is this love,
Bm7
Is this love that I'm feeling?

Link 2

| Bm7 A/C♯ | D E |
D
Oh yes I know, yes I know, yes I know now.

| Bm7 A/C♯ | D E |
Amaj7
Oh yes I know, yes I know, yes I know now.

Bridge 2 As Bridge 1

Verse 3 As Verse 2 *Fade out*

Jamming

Words & Music by
Bob Marley

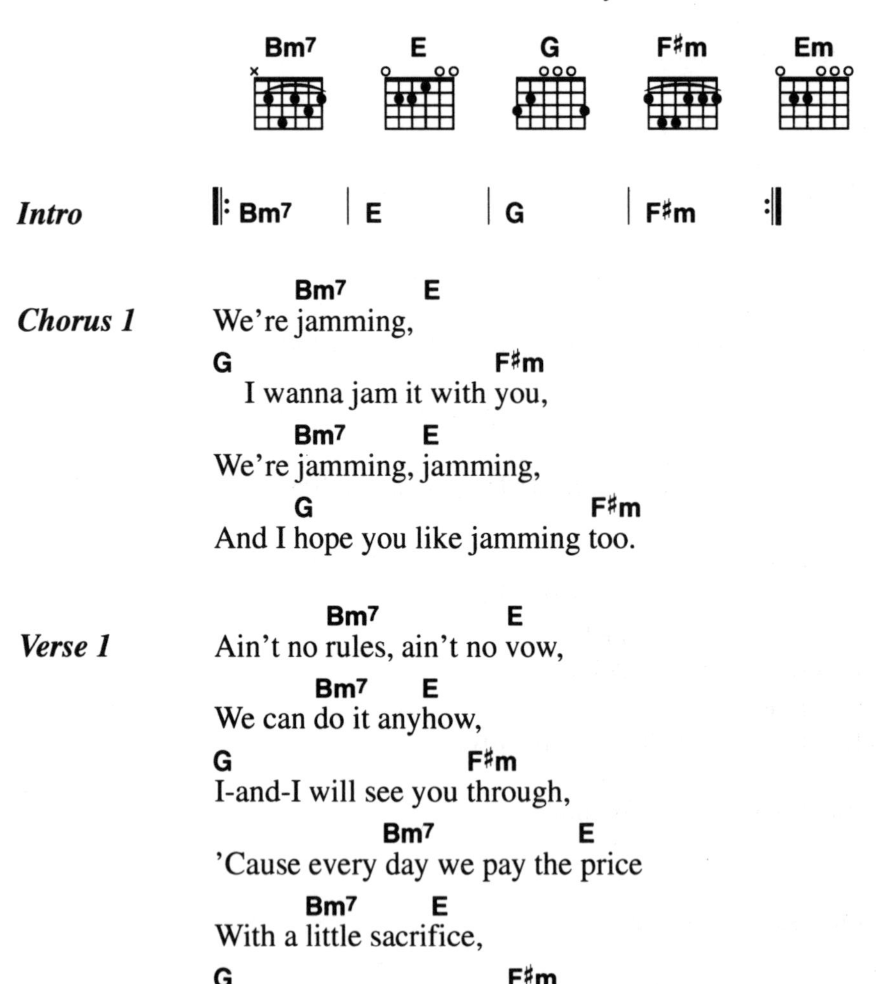

Intro ‖: Bm7 | E | G | F♯m :‖

Chorus 1

```
         Bm7       E
We're jamming,
G                        F♯m
   I wanna jam it with you,
         Bm7       E
We're jamming, jamming,
     G                            F♯m
And I hope you like jamming too.
```

Verse 1

```
              Bm7            E
Ain't no rules, ain't no vow,
             Bm7      E
We can do it anyhow,
G                         F♯m
I-and-I will see you through,
                    Bm7             E
'Cause every day we pay the price
           Bm7        E
With a little sacrifice,
G                         F♯m
Jamming till the jam is through.
```

Chorus 2

```
         Bm7       E
We're jamming,
                   G                        F♯m
To think that jamming was a thing of the past,
         Bm7       E
We're jamming,
     G                          F♯m
And I hope this jam is gonna last.
```

Verse 2

Bm7 E
No bullet can stop us now,

Bm7 E
We neither beg nor we won't bow,

G F♯m
Neither can be bought nor sold.

Bm7 E
We all defend the right,

Bm7 E
JAH JAH children must unite,

G F♯m
Your life is worth much more than gold.

Chorus 3

Bm7
We're jamming,

E
(Jamming, jamming, jamming,)

G F♯m
And we're jamming in the name of the Lord,

Bm7
We're jamming,

E
(Jamming, jamming, jamming,)

G F♯m
We're jamming right straight from JAH.

Bridge

Bm7 Em
Holy Mount Zion,

Bm7 Em
Holy Mount Zion.

Bm7 N.C.
JAH sitteth in Mount Zion

Bm7 N.C.
And rules all Creation.

Chorus 4

Bm7
Yeah, we're jamming,

E Bm7
(Pop-choo), pop-choo-wa-wa,

Bm7
We're jamming (pop-choo-wa), see?

G F♯m
I wanna jam it with you.

cont.

```
          Bm7
We're jamming,
            E
(Jamming, jamming, jamming,)
    G                              F#m
I'm jammed, I hope you're jamming too.
```

Verse 3

```
Bm7             E          Bm7          E
Jam's about my pride and truth I cannot hide
G                  F#m
   To keep you satisfied.
      Bm7            E         Bm7        E
True love that now exist is the love I can't resist
   G            F#m
So   jam by my side.
```

Chorus 5

```
                Bm7
||: Yeah, we're jamming,
            E
(Jamming, jamming, jamming)
G                  F#m
   I wanna jam it with you.
       Bm7
We're jamming, we're jamming,

We're jamming, we're jamming,
       E
We're jamming, we're jamming,

We're jamming, we're jamming,
G                      F#m
   Hope you like jamming too.  :||  Repeat to end with ad lib. vocals
```

No Woman, No Cry

Words & Music by
Bob Marley & Vincent Ford

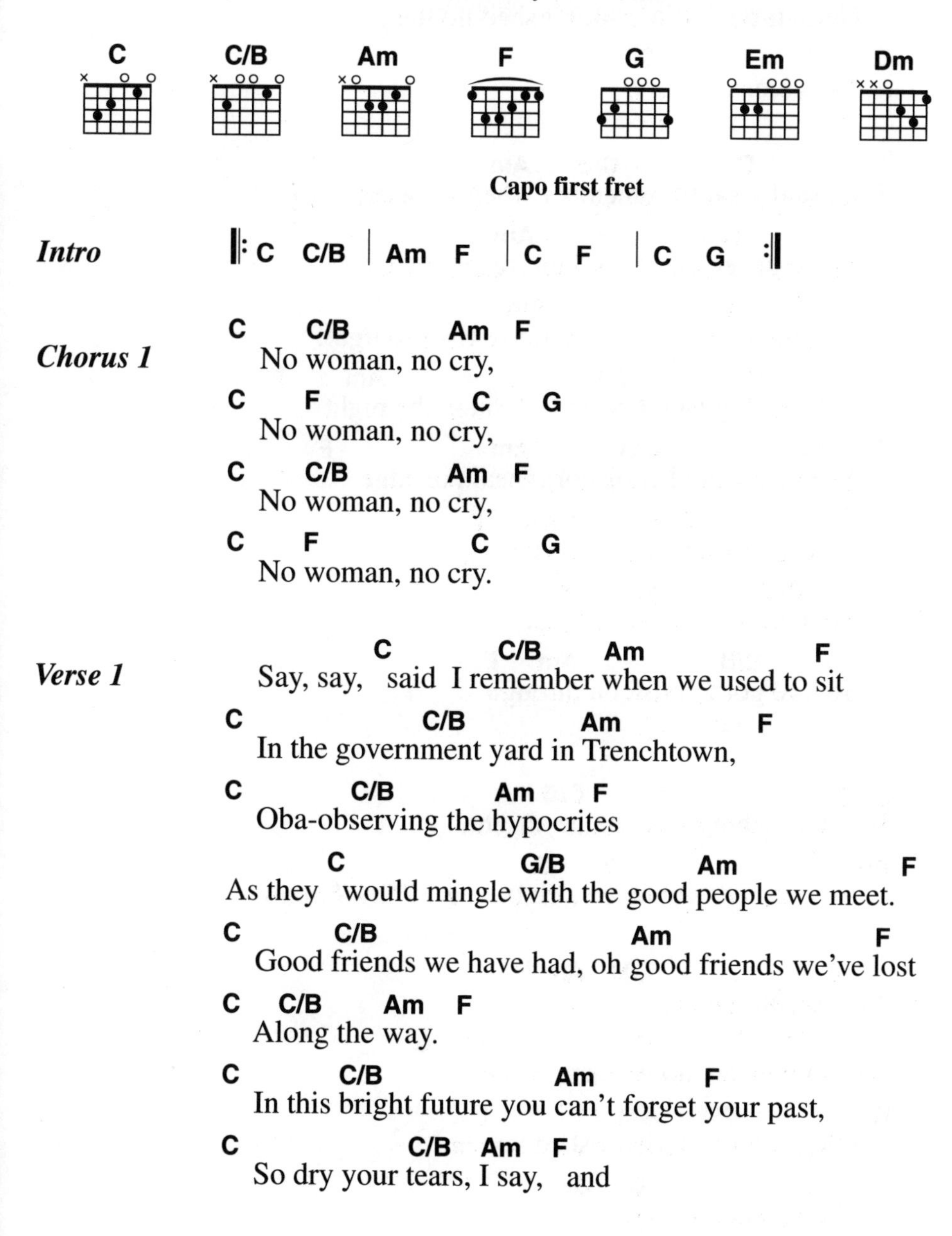

Capo first fret

Intro

```
||: C   C/B | Am   F | C   F | C   G :||
```

Chorus 1

```
C     C/B         Am  F
  No woman, no cry,
C     F           C    G
  No woman, no cry,
C     C/B         Am  F
  No woman, no cry,
C     F           C    G
  No woman, no cry.
```

Verse 1

```
                C          C/B      Am              F
  Say, say,   said  I remember when we used to sit
C                 C/B          Am            F
  In the government yard in Trenchtown,
C          C/B          Am     F
  Oba-observing the hypocrites
          C              G/B          Am                 F
As they   would mingle with the good people we meet.
C         C/B                        Am               F
  Good friends we have had, oh good friends we've lost
C   C/B    Am   F
  Along the way.
C         C/B                   Am          F
  In this bright future you can't forget your past,
C                  C/B  Am   F
  So dry your tears, I say,   and
```

Chorus 2

```
C     C/B        Am F
   No woman, no cry,
C     F             C     G
   No woman, no cry,
C     C/B             Am          F
   Here  little darlin',   don't shed no tears,
C     F             C   G
   No woman, no cry.
```

Verse 2

```
               C          C/B     Am               F
Said, said,   said I remember when we used to sit
C            C/B                 Am          F
   In the government yard in Trenchtown,
C              C/B               Am            F
   And then Georgie would make the fire light
             C          C/B                  Am       F
As it was   log wood burnin' through the night.
C                    C/B      Am               F
   Then we would cook corn meal porridge
C                 C/B          Am    F
   Of which I'll share with you.
C        C/B        Am       F
   My feet is my only carriage
C           C/B               Am    F
   So I've got to push on through.
```

Bridge

```
  C                     C/B
‖:   Ev'rything's gonna be alright,
Am                         F    G
   Ev'rything's gonna be alright.  :‖   Play 4 times
```

Chorus 3

```
   C                 C/B   Am  F
No woman, no cry,
          C           F              C    G
No, no woman, no woman, no cry.
C          C/B    Am             F
   Oh, little sister, don't shed no tears,
C     F             C   G
   No woman, no cry.
```

Solo

```
‖: C   C/B | Am   F | C   F | C   G :‖   Play 4 times
```

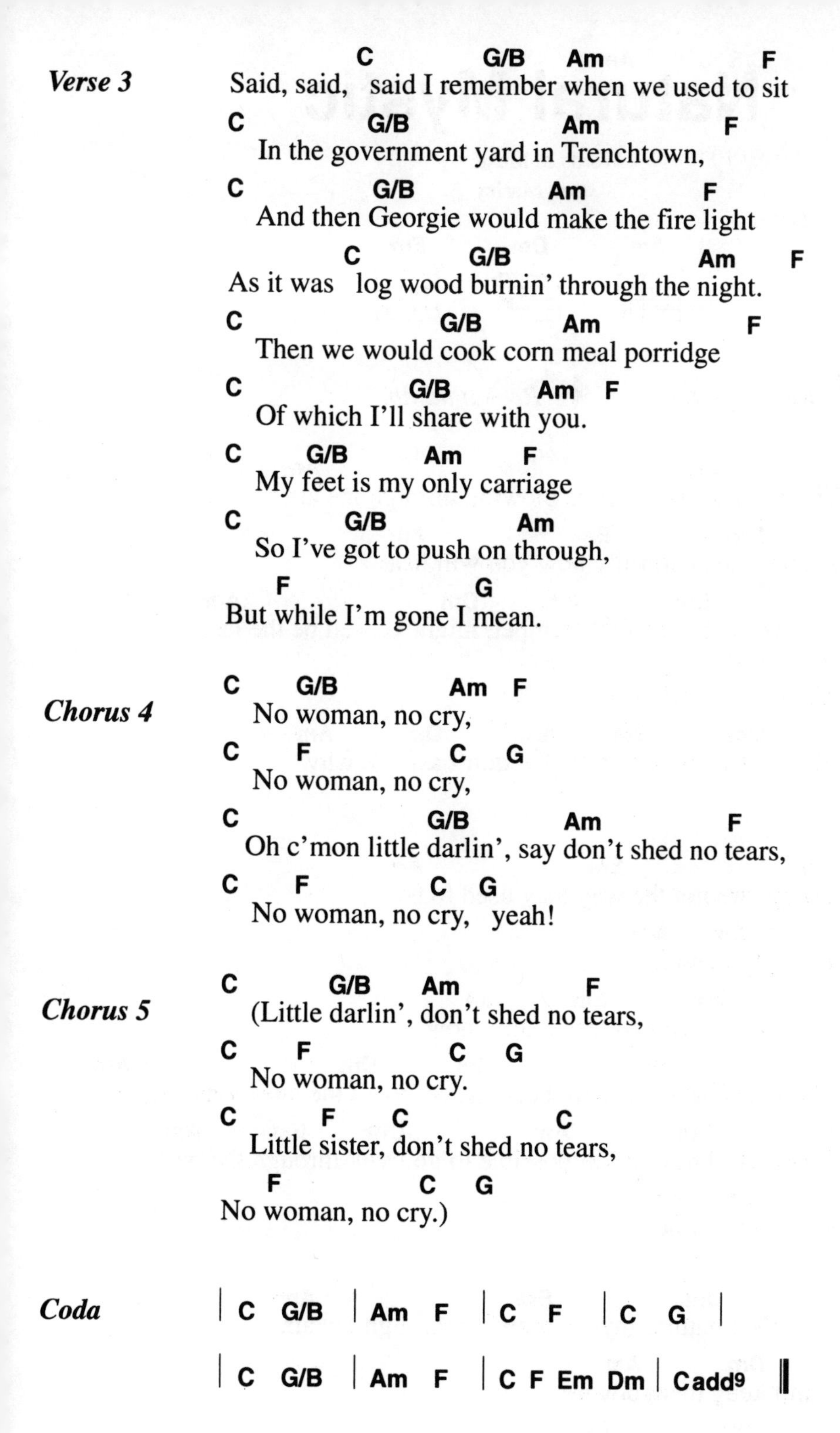

```
                  C          G/B     Am           F
Verse 3     Said, said,  said I remember when we used to sit
            C       G/B              Am           F
              In the government yard in Trenchtown,
            C          G/B         Am          F
              And then Georgie would make the fire light
                    C         G/B                   Am      F
            As it was  log wood burnin' through the night.
            C                   G/B       Am             F
              Then we would cook corn meal porridge
            C              G/B      Am   F
              Of which I'll share with you.
            C      G/B        Am     F
              My feet is my only carriage
            C          G/B         Am
              So I've got to push on through,
               F                G
            But while I'm gone I mean.

            C    G/B          Am  F
Chorus 4      No woman, no cry,
            C    F            C   G
              No woman, no cry,
            C                   G/B      Am          F
             Oh c'mon little darlin', say don't shed no tears,
            C    F           C  G
              No woman, no cry,   yeah!

            C       G/B     Am           F
Chorus 5      (Little darlin', don't shed no tears,
            C    F            C   G
              No woman, no cry.
            C       F    C             C
              Little sister, don't shed no tears,
              F             C   G
            No woman, no cry.)

Coda        | C  G/B  | Am  F  | C  F  | C  G |

            | C  G/B  | Am  F  | C F Em Dm | Cadd9 ||
```

Natural Mystic

Words & Music by
Bob Marley

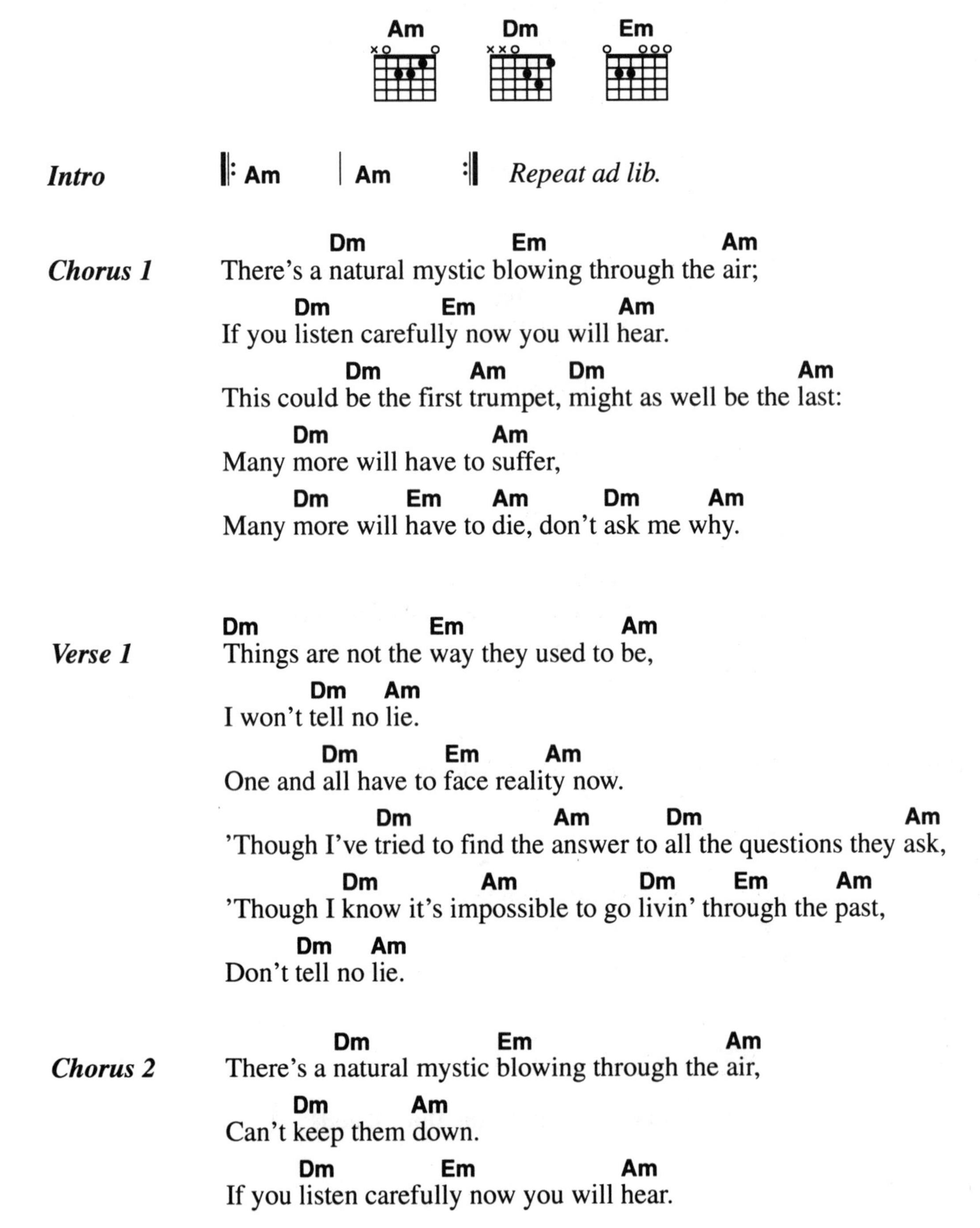

Link | Am | Am ||

Verse 2

Dm Am Dm Am
This could be the first trumpet, might as well be the last:
Dm Am
Many more will have to suffer,
Dm Em Am Dm Am
Many more will have to die, don't ask me why.

Coda

Dm Em Am
There's a natural mystic blowing through the air,
Dm Am
I won't tell no lie.
Dm Em Am
If you listen carefully now you will hear:
Dm Em Am
There's a natural mystic blowing through the air.

Such a natural mystic blowing through the air;

There's a natural mystic blowing through the air;

Such a natural mystic blowing through the air. *Fade out*

One Love

Words & Music by
Bob Marley

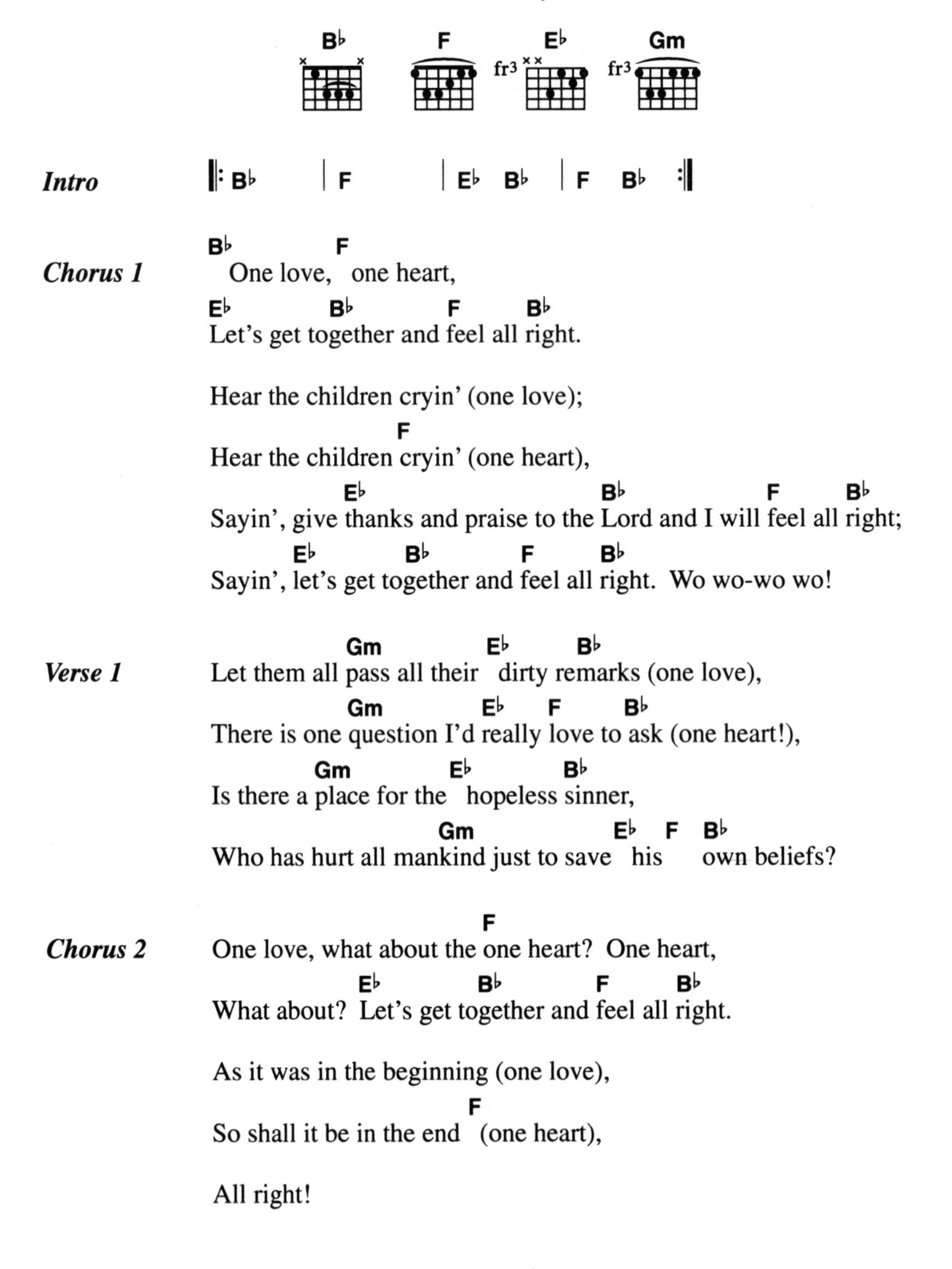

Bb F Eb Gm

Intro ||: Bb | F | Eb Bb | F Bb :||

Chorus 1

Bb F
One love, one heart,
Eb Bb F Bb
Let's get together and feel all right.

Hear the children cryin' (one love);
F
Hear the children cryin' (one heart),
Eb Bb F Bb
Sayin', give thanks and praise to the Lord and I will feel all right;
Eb Bb F Bb
Sayin', let's get together and feel all right. Wo wo-wo wo!

Verse 1

Gm Eb Bb
Let them all pass all their dirty remarks (one love),
Gm Eb F Bb
There is one question I'd really love to ask (one heart!),
Gm Eb Bb
Is there a place for the hopeless sinner,
Gm Eb F Bb
Who has hurt all mankind just to save his own beliefs?

Chorus 2

F
One love, what about the one heart? One heart,
Eb Bb F Bb
What about? Let's get together and feel all right.

As it was in the beginning (one love),
F
So shall it be in the end (one heart),

All right!

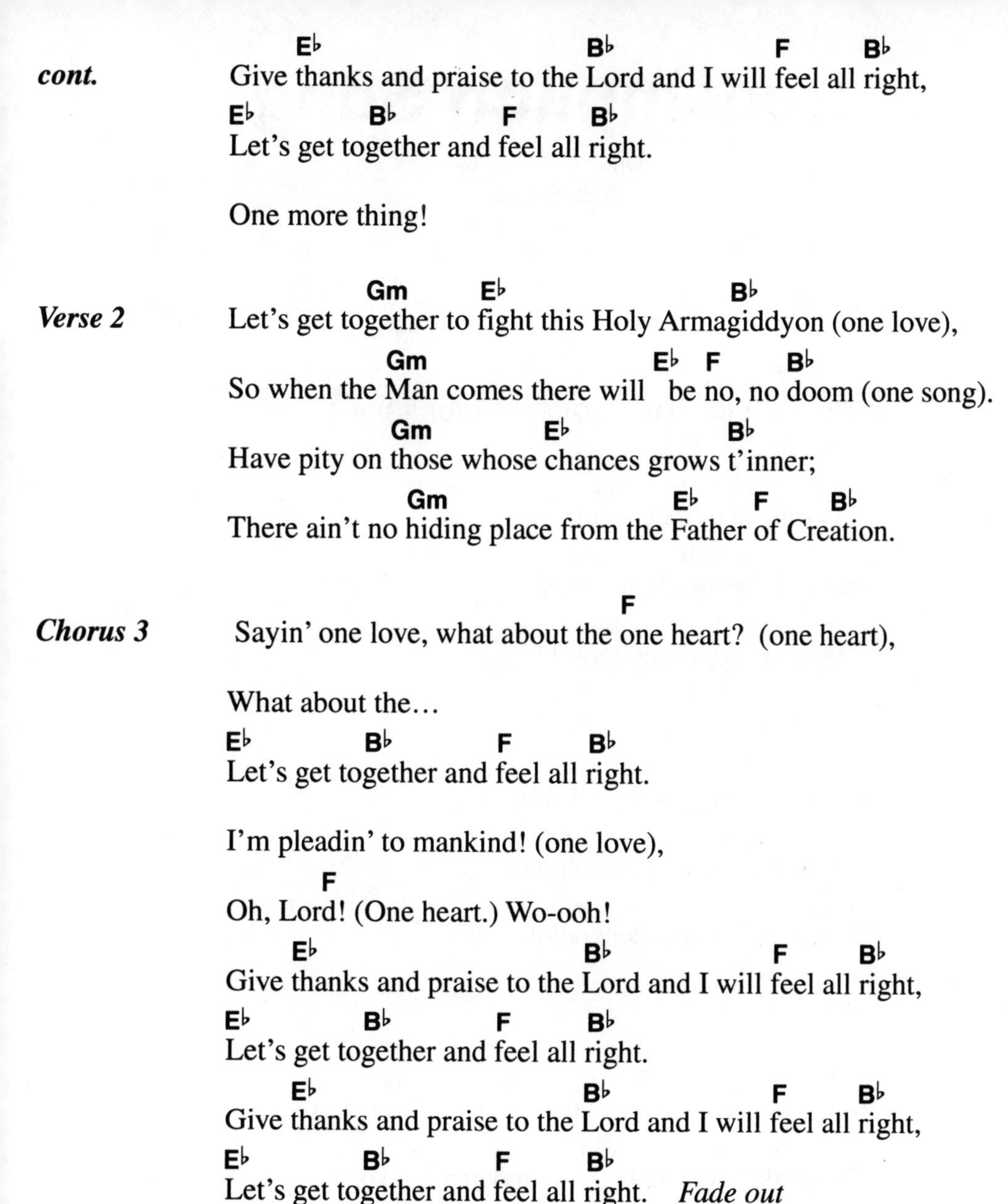

cont.

E♭ B♭ F B♭
Give thanks and praise to the Lord and I will feel all right,

E♭ B♭ F B♭
Let's get together and feel all right.

One more thing!

Verse 2

Gm E♭ B♭
Let's get together to fight this Holy Armagiddyon (one love),

Gm E♭ F B♭
So when the Man comes there will be no, no doom (one song).

Gm E♭ B♭
Have pity on those whose chances grows t'inner;

Gm E♭ F B♭
There ain't no hiding place from the Father of Creation.

Chorus 3

F
Sayin' one love, what about the one heart? (one heart),

What about the…

E♭ B♭ F B♭
Let's get together and feel all right.

I'm pleadin' to mankind! (one love),

F
Oh, Lord! (One heart.) Wo-ooh!

E♭ B♭ F B♭
Give thanks and praise to the Lord and I will feel all right,

E♭ B♭ F B♭
Let's get together and feel all right.

E♭ B♭ F B♭
Give thanks and praise to the Lord and I will feel all right,

E♭ B♭ F B♭
Let's get together and feel all right. *Fade out*

Redemption Song

Words & Music by
Bob Marley

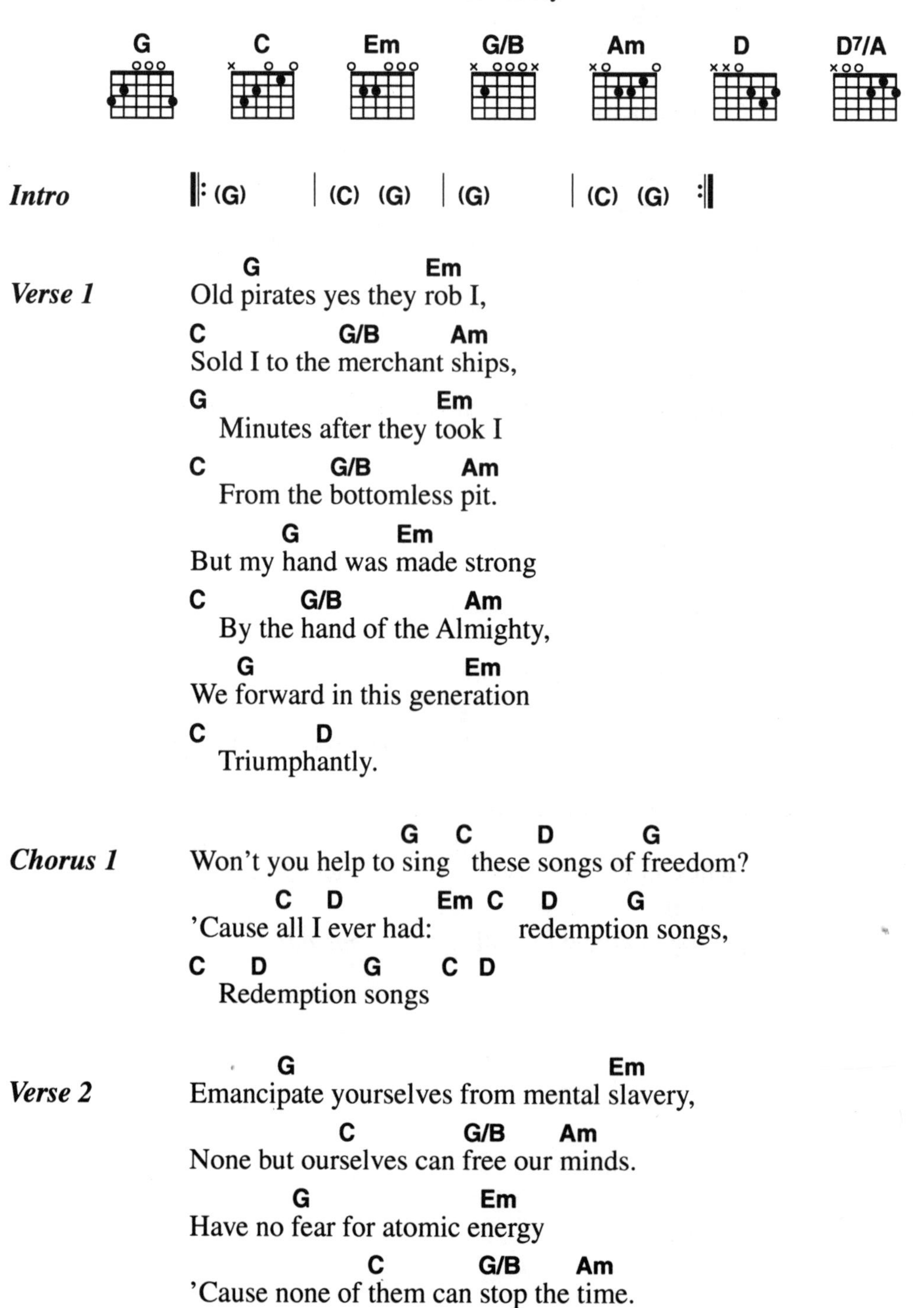

G C Em G/B Am D D7/A

```
Intro     |: (G)       | (C)  (G)  | (G)        | (C)  (G)  :|

Verse 1        G                  Em
          Old pirates yes they rob I,
          C               G/B         Am
          Sold I to the merchant ships,
          G                          Em
             Minutes after they took I
          C              G/B           Am
             From the bottomless pit.
                 G            Em
          But my hand was made strong
          C        G/B               Am
             By the hand of the Almighty,
              G                      Em
          We forward in this generation
          C             D
             Triumphantly.

Chorus 1                          G    C       D          G
          Won't you help to sing   these songs of freedom?
                    C    D            Em  C     D        G
          'Cause all I ever had:             redemption songs,
          C     D          G        C   D
             Redemption songs

Verse 2         G                                    Em
          Emancipate yourselves from mental slavery,
                             C          G/B       Am
          None but ourselves can free our minds.
                    G                   Em
          Have no fear for atomic energy
                               C          G/B       Am
          'Cause none of them can stop the time.
```

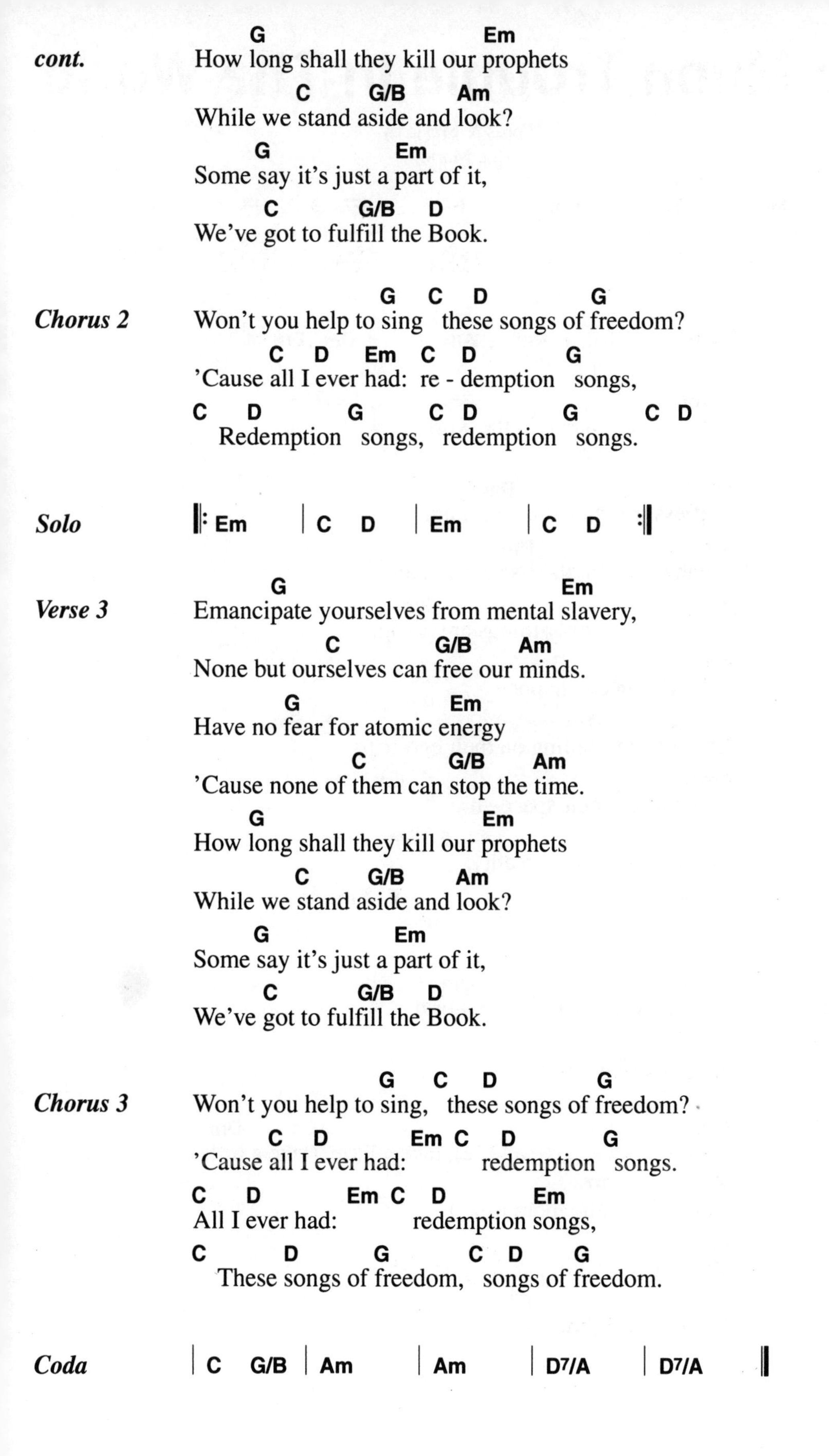

```
            G                         Em
cont.       How long shall they kill our prophets
                 C      G/B     Am
            While we stand aside and look?
              G              Em
            Some say it's just a part of it,
               C         G/B    D
            We've got to fulfill the Book.


                             G    C    D         G
Chorus 2    Won't you help to sing   these songs of freedom?
                C    D    Em   C    D         G
            'Cause all I ever had:  re - demption   songs,
            C    D        G       C   D        G       C   D
              Redemption   songs,  redemption   songs.


Solo        |: Em      | C    D   | Em      | C    D   :|


                G                            Em
Verse 3     Emancipate yourselves from mental slavery,
                      C         G/B      Am
            None but ourselves can free our minds.
                 G                 Em
            Have no fear for atomic energy
                        C         G/B      Am
            'Cause none of them can stop the time.
              G                    Em
            How long shall they kill our prophets
                 C      G/B     Am
            While we stand aside and look?
              G              Em
            Some say it's just a part of it,
               C         G/B    D
            We've got to fulfill the Book.


                             G    C    D         G
Chorus 3    Won't you help to sing,   these songs of freedom?
                C    D          Em C    D         G
            'Cause all I ever had:         redemption   songs.
            C    D         Em C    D          Em
            All I ever had:        redemption songs,
            C        D        G          C   D      G
              These songs of freedom,   songs of freedom.


Coda        | C   G/B | Am      | Am      | D7/A     | D7/A     ||
```

So Much Trouble In The World

Words & Music by
Bob Marley

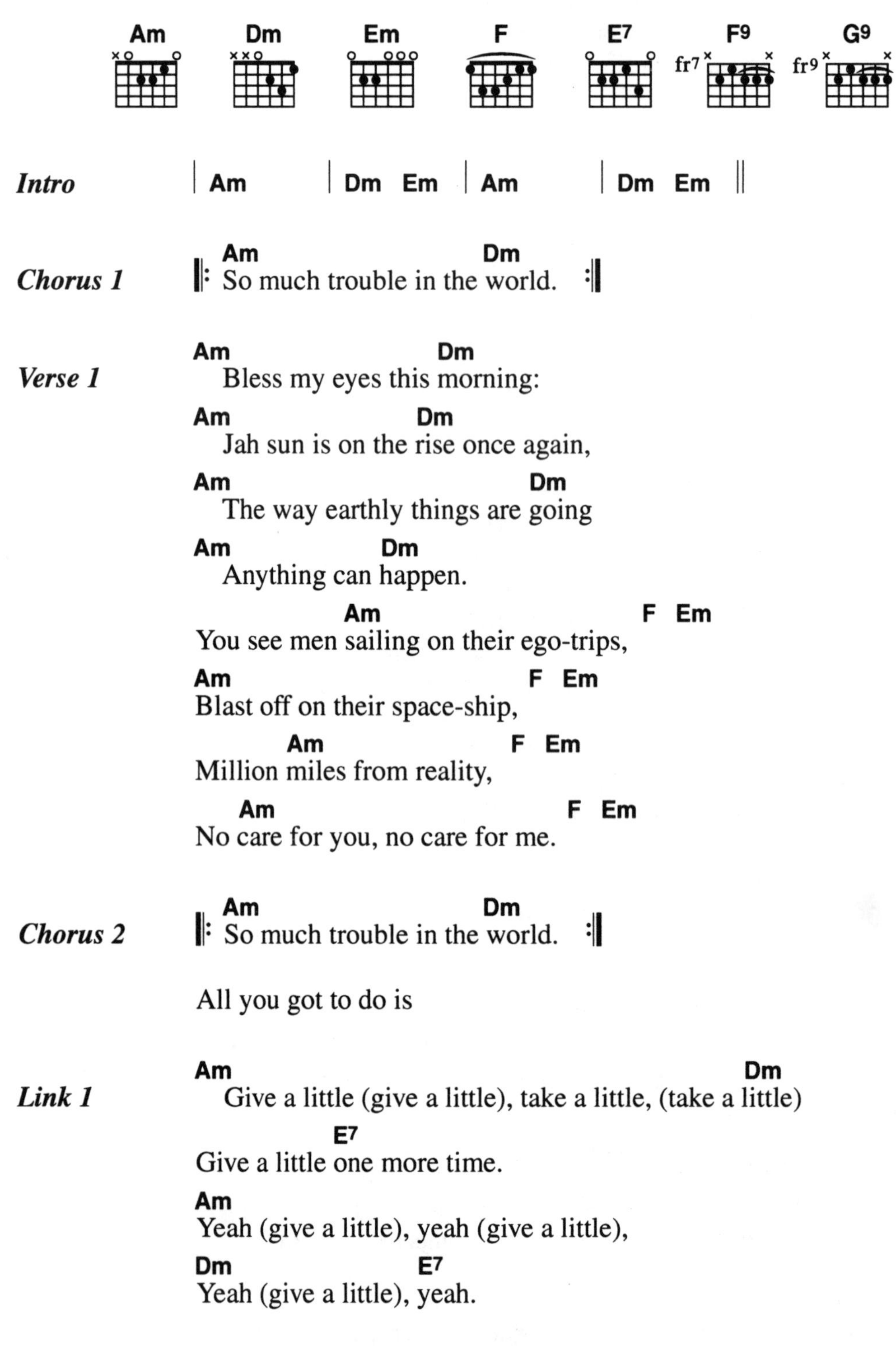

Intro | Am | Dm Em | Am | Dm Em ||

```
            Am                          Dm
Chorus 1  ||: So much trouble in the world.  :||

          Am                 Dm
Verse 1     Bless my eyes this morning:
          Am              Dm
            Jah sun is on the rise once again,
          Am                          Dm
            The way earthly things are going
          Am           Dm
            Anything can happen.
                         Am                          F  Em
          You see men sailing on their ego-trips,
          Am                             F  Em
          Blast off on their space-ship,
                    Am                  F  Em
          Million miles from reality,
             Am                         F  Em
          No care for you, no care for me.

            Am                          Dm
Chorus 2  ||: So much trouble in the world.  :||

          All you got to do is

          Am                                                       Dm
Link 1      Give a little (give a little), take a little, (take a little)
                         E7
          Give a little one more time.
          Am
          Yeah (give a little), yeah (give a little),
          Dm                    E7
          Yeah (give a little), yeah.
```

Bridge

F⁹
So you think you have found the solution
But it's just another illusion,
So before you check out this time
G⁹
Don't leave another cornerstone
Standing there behind.

Verse 2

Am Dm
We've got to face the day,
Am Dm
Ooh-we, come what may.
Am Dm
We the street people talking,
Am Dm
We the people struggling.

Link 2

| Am | Dm Em | Am | Dm Em ||

Verse 3

Am F Em
Now they are sitting on a time-bomb,
Am F Em
Now I know the time has come,
Am F Em
What goes on up is coming on down,
Am F Em
Goes around and comes around.

Chorus 3

Am Dm
𝄆 So much trouble in the world. 𝄇 *Play 3 times*

Coda

Am
There is so much trouble,
Dm
There is so much trouble,
Am
There is so much trouble,
Dm
There is so much trouble in the world,
Am Dm
There is so much trouble in the world. *Fade out*

Stir It Up

Words & Music by
Bob Marley

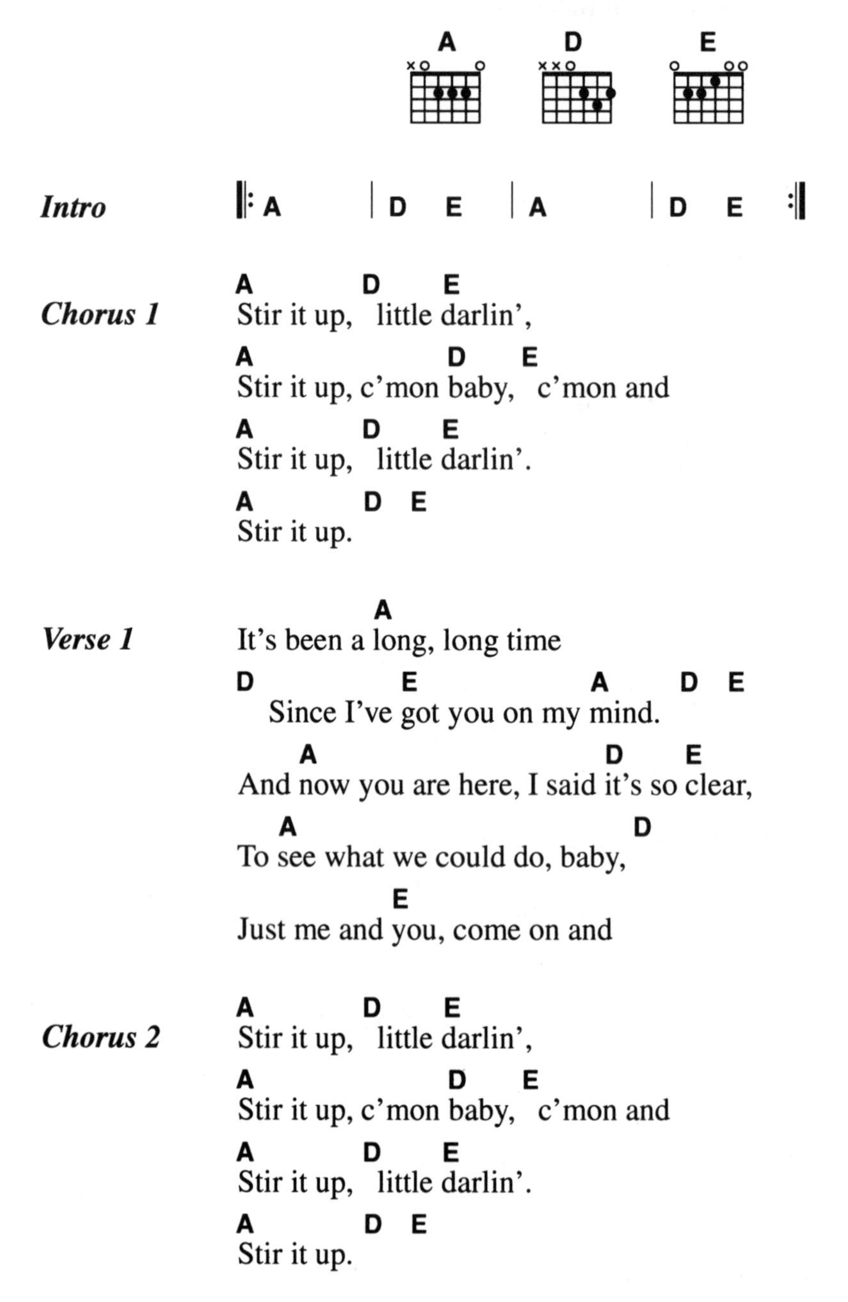


```
Intro        |: A       | D   E  | A       | D   E  :|

             A        D     E
Chorus 1     Stir it up,  little darlin',
             A                D      E
             Stir it up, c'mon baby,  c'mon and
             A        D     E
             Stir it up,  little darlin'.
             A        D  E
             Stir it up.

                         A
Verse 1      It's been a long, long time
             D              E                  A       D   E
               Since I've got you on my mind.
                 A                         D      E
             And now you are here, I said it's so clear,
                A                                D
             To see what we could do, baby,
                           E
             Just me and you, come on and

             A        D     E
Chorus 2     Stir it up,  little darlin',
             A                D      E
             Stir it up, c'mon baby,  c'mon and
             A        D     E
             Stir it up,  little darlin'.
             A        D  E
             Stir it up.
```

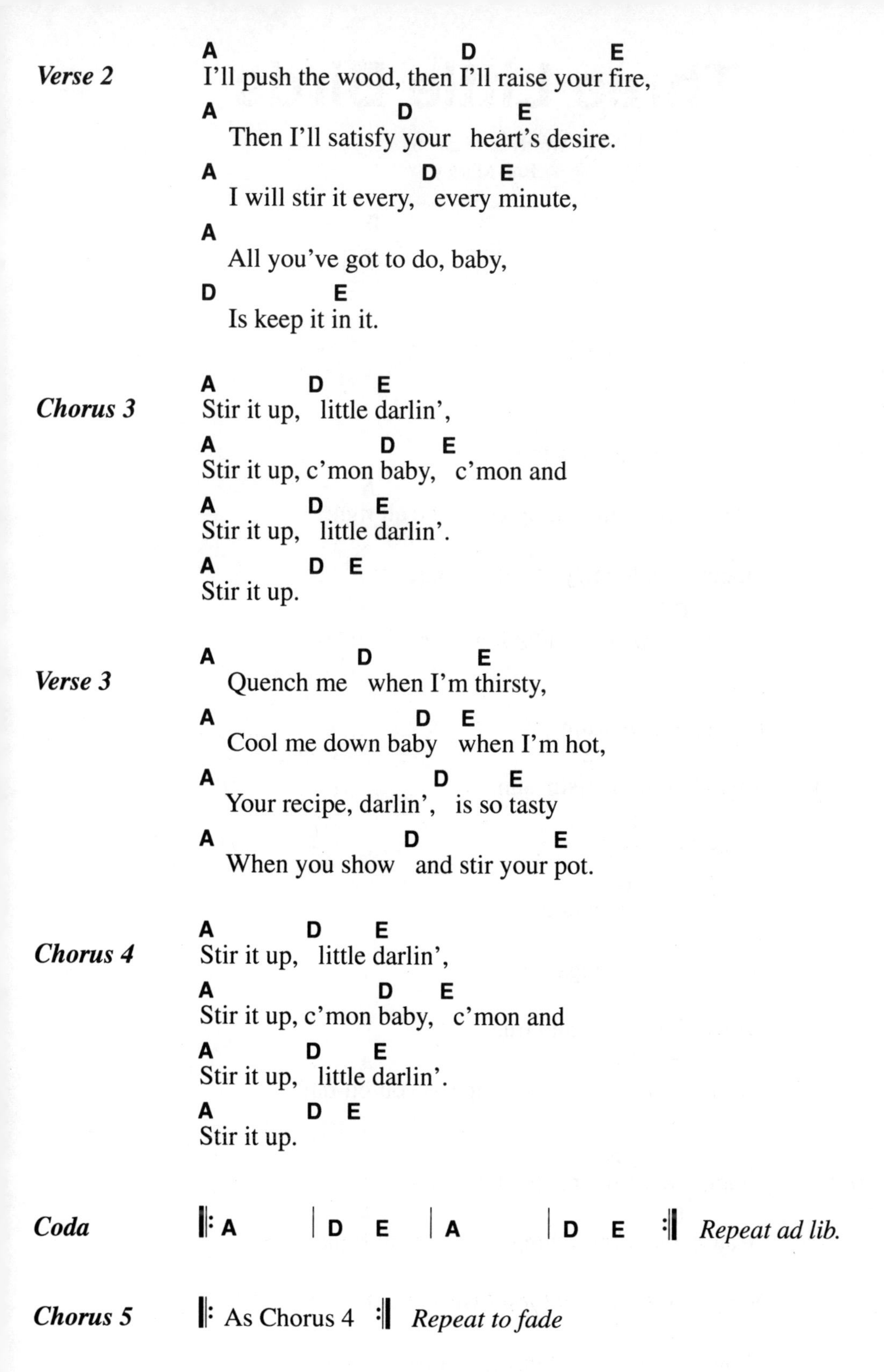

```
           A                       D              E
Verse 2    I'll push the wood, then I'll raise your fire,
           A                  D        E
              Then I'll satisfy your   heart's desire.
           A                     D      E
              I will stir it every,   every minute,
           A
              All you've got to do, baby,
           D            E
              Is keep it in it.

           A         D       E
Chorus 3   Stir it up,   little darlin',
           A                     D      E
           Stir it up, c'mon baby,   c'mon and
           A         D       E
           Stir it up,   little darlin'.
           A         D    E
           Stir it up.

           A              D             E
Verse 3       Quench me   when I'm thirsty,
           A                       D     E
              Cool me down baby   when I'm hot,
           A                          D        E
              Your recipe, darlin',   is so tasty
           A                      D             E
              When you show   and stir your pot.

           A         D       E
Chorus 4   Stir it up,   little darlin',
           A                     D      E
           Stir it up, c'mon baby,   c'mon and
           A         D       E
           Stir it up,   little darlin'.
           A         D    E
           Stir it up.

Coda       |: A       | D    E   | A        | D    E   :|   Repeat ad lib.

Chorus 5   |: As Chorus 4 :|   Repeat to fade
```

Three Little Birds

Words & Music by
Bob Marley

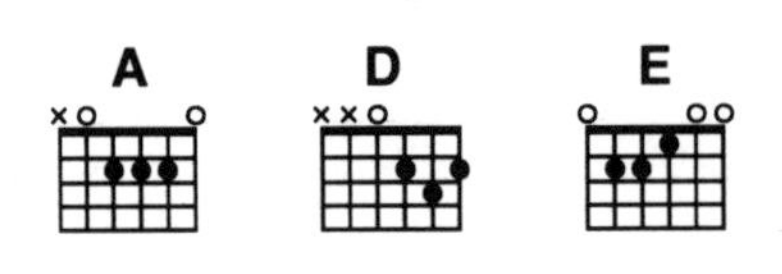

Intro | A | A | A | A ||

Chorus 1

```
          A
Don't worry about a thing,
           D                          A
'Cause every little thing gonna be all right.

Singin' don't worry about a thing,
           D                          A
'Cause every little thing gonna be all right!
```

Verse 1

```
                 A
Rise up this mornin',
                    E
Smiled with the risin' sun,
                A
Three little birds
                 D
Pitch by my doorstep
          A
Singin' sweet songs
                E
Of melodies pure and true,
           D                          A
Sayin',  "This is my message to you-ou-ou:"
```

Chorus 2

```
                   A
Singin' don't worry 'bout a thing,
           D                          A
'Cause every little thing gonna be all right.

Singin' don't worry (don't worry) 'bout a thing,
           D                          A
'Cause every little thing gonna be all right!
```

```
                        A
Verse 2      Rise up this mornin',
                             E
             Smiled with the risin' sun,
                       A
             Three little birds
                        D
             Pitch by my doorstep
                 A
             Singin' sweet songs
                        E
             Of melodies pure and true,
                 D                          A
             Sayin',  "This is my message to you-ou-ou:"

                           A
Chorus 3     |: Singin' don't worry about a thing, worry about a thing, oh!
             D                             A
             Every little thing gonna be all right, don't worry!

             Singin' don't worry about a thing, I won't worry!
                 D                             A
             'Cause every little thing gonna be all right. :|   Repeat to fade
```

Waiting in Vain

Words & Music by
Bob Marley

A♭maj7 fr4 | D♭maj7 fr4 | D♭ fr4 | E♭ fr6 | Cm7 fr3 | B♭m7

Intro | A♭maj7 | D♭maj7 | A♭maj7 | D♭maj7 ||

```
           A♭maj7               D♭maj7
Chorus 1   I don't wanna wait in vain for your love;
           A♭maj7               D♭maj7
           I don't wanna wait in vain for your love.

           A♭maj7                          D♭maj7
Verse 1      From the very first time I rest my eyes on you, girl,
           A♭maj7                     D♭maj7
             My heart says follow through.
           A♭maj7                          D♭maj7
             But I know, now, that I'm way down on your line,
           A♭maj7                     D♭maj7
             But the waitin' feel is fine:
           A♭maj7                        D♭maj7
             So don't treat me like a puppet on a string,
           A♭maj7                                  D♭maj7
             'Cause I know I have to do my thing.
           A♭maj7                    D♭maj7
             Don't talk to me as if you think I'm dumb;
           A♭maj7                                      D♭maj7
             I wanna know when you're gonna come.

                A♭maj7                  D♭maj7
Chorus 2   See, I don't wanna wait in vain for your love;
           A♭maj7               D♭maj7
           I don't wanna wait in vain for your love;
           A♭maj7               D♭maj7
           I don't wanna wait in vain for your love,
```

Bridge

Db Eb
'Cause if summer is here,
Cm7 Bbm7
I'm still waiting there;
Db Eb
Winter is here,
Cm7 Bbm7
And I'm still waiting there.

Solo

| Abmaj7 | Dbmaj7 | Abmaj7 | Dbmaj7 |

| Abmaj7 | Dbmaj7 | Abmaj7 | Dbmaj7 ||
Like I said:

Verse 2

Abmaj7 Dbmaj7
It's been three years since I'm knockin' on your door,
Abmaj7 Dbmaj7
And I still can knock some more:
Abmaj7 Dbmaj7
Ooh girl, ooh girl, is it feasible? I wanna know now,
Abmaj7 Dbmaj7
For I to knock some more.
Abmaj7 Dbmaj7
Ya see, in life I know there's lots of grief,
Abmaj7 Dbmaj7
But your love is my relief:
Abmaj7 Dbmaj7
Tears in my eyes burn, tears in my eyes burn
Abmaj7 Dbmaj7
While I'm waiting, while I'm waiting for my turn,

See!

Chorus 3

Abmaj7 Dbmaj7
||: I don't wanna wait in vain for your love;
Abmaj7 Dbmaj7
I don't wanna wait in vain for your love, oh! :|| *Play 4 times*

Coda

Abmaj7
||: I don't wanna, I don't wanna, I don't wanna, I don't wanna,
Dbmaj7
I don't wanna wait in vain. :|| *Play 4 times*
Abmaj7
||: It's your love that I'm waiting on,
Dbmaj7
It's my love that you're running from. :|| *Repeat to fade*

Satisfy My Soul

Words & Music by
Bob Marley

Gmaj7 Bm Am D G C

Intro | Gmaj7 Bm | Am D | Gmaj7 Bm | Am D ||

Chorus 1

```
      Gmaj7              Bm   Am
Oh, please don't you rock my boat
         D
(Don't rock my boat),
           Gmaj7   Bm             Am
'Cause I don't    want my boat to be rockin'
         D
(Don't rock my boat).
      Gmaj7  Bm                 Am
Oh, please  don't you rock my boat
         D
(Don't rock my boat),
           Gmaj7   Bm             Am
'Cause I don't    want my boat to be rockin'
         D
(Don't rock my boat).
```

Verse 1

```
                            C
I'm telling you that,   oh, oh-ooh, wo-o-wo!
                          D
I like it, like it like this (I like it like this),

So keep it steady, like this (I like it like this).
                      C
And you should know, you should know by now
             D
I like it (I like it like this), I like it like this,

 (I like it like this, I like it like this),

I like it like this, ooh yeah!
```

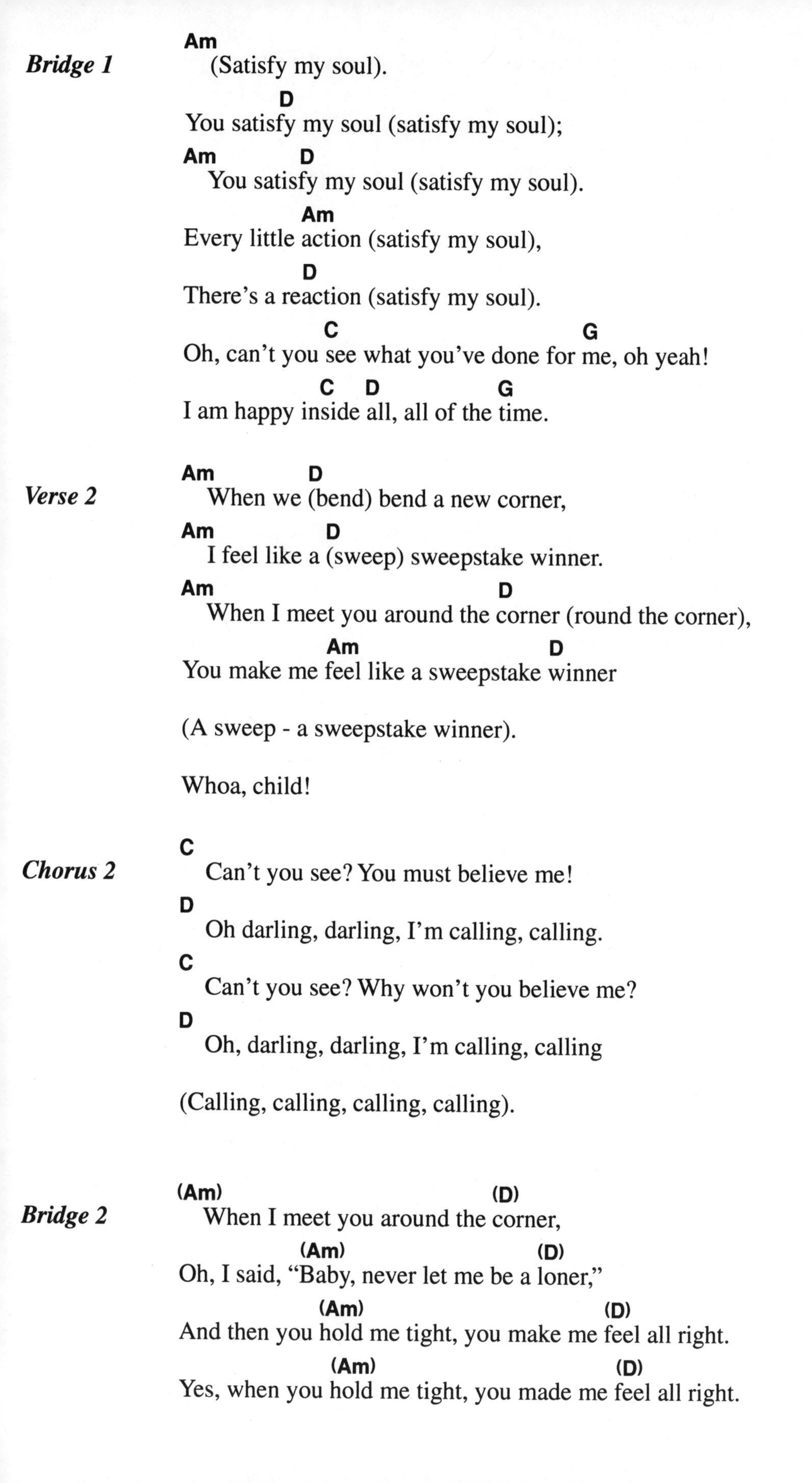

```
            Am
Bridge 1       (Satisfy my soul).
                    D
            You satisfy my soul (satisfy my soul);
            Am         D
               You satisfy my soul (satisfy my soul).
                          Am
            Every little action (satisfy my soul),
                          D
            There's a reaction (satisfy my soul).
                            C                          G
            Oh, can't you see what you've done for me, oh yeah!
                           C    D               G
            I am happy inside all, all of the time.

            Am          D
Verse 2        When we (bend) bend a new corner,
            Am              D
               I feel like a (sweep) sweepstake winner.
            Am                                  D
               When I meet you around the corner (round the corner),
                            Am                     D
            You make me feel like a sweepstake winner

            (A sweep - a sweepstake winner).

            Whoa, child!

            C
Chorus 2       Can't you see? You must believe me!
            D
               Oh darling, darling, I'm calling, calling.
            C
               Can't you see? Why won't you believe me?
            D
               Oh, darling, darling, I'm calling, calling

            (Calling, calling, calling, calling).

            (Am)                            (D)
Bridge 2       When I meet you around the corner,
                         (Am)                  (D)
            Oh, I said, "Baby, never let me be a loner,"
                            (Am)                        (D)
            And then you hold me tight, you make me feel all right.
                             (Am)                         (D)
            Yes, when you hold me tight, you made me feel all right.
```

Chorus 3

```
         C
Whoa,    can't you see? Don't you believe me?
D
   Oh, darling, darling, I'm callin', callin'.
C
   Can't you see? Why won't you believe me?
D
   Oh, darling, darling, I'm callin', callin',
```

(Calling, calling, calling, calling).

Coda

```
Am
   Satisfy my soul,
D
   Satisfy my soul,
Am
   Satisfy my soul,
D
   Satisfy my soul.
Am
   That's all I want you to do,
D
   That's all I'll take from you.
```

Fade out

1/03 (46527)